RICK SIMPSON OIL

NATURE'S ANSWER FOR CANCER

Rick Simpson

SIMPSON
RAMADUR

2018

Title
Rick Simpson Oil – Nature's Answer for Cancer

Author
Rick Simpson

Third Edition
Copyright © Rick Simpson, 2013

Cover Layout
Lana Oresic

Cover Art
Den Beauvais

Rick's photo
Davor Pongracic

Publisher
Simpson RamaDur d.o.o., Jurja Dobrile 20, 10000 Zagreb, Croatia
www.simpsonramadur.com

Rick Simpson and Danijela Smiljanić Simpson would like to thank all who were involved in getting this book ready for publication.

ISBN 978-9-5358-7512-3
A CIP catalogue record for this book is available from the National and University Library Zagreb under the number 000998736.

DISCLAIMER
We bear no responsibility if this information is misused and it is provided for educational purposes only.

DEDICATION

I would like to dedicate this book to the memory of everyone that is no longer with us, who have suffered and died due the incompetence and corruption of those we are supposed to be able to trust.

Rick Simpson, November 2012.

Contents

═══════

PREFACE

I have been providing high quality medicinal extracts and instructions to patients, explaining how they too can produce hemp oil medicines themselves, since 2003. The results have truly been nothing short of amazing and now vast numbers of people worldwide have finally learned what has been hidden from us for so long.

Throughout history, cannabis hemp has proven itself to be the most medicinally active plant that we have at our disposal. Its use as a medicine has achieved legendary status because it is perfectly safe and no one has ever died from its effects. Since it produces medicines, which are so harmless, safe, and effective, why in heaven's name are we not putting this plant to good use, doing what it does best?

Statements to this effect have been voiced by many highly respected individuals in the field of medicine and elsewhere for decades but sadly it often seems that no one is listening, even though knowledge of hemp's healing virtues was quite widely known long before the time of Jesus and I strongly suspect that he himself used extracts this plant can produce to heal the masses. Since that time, knowledge about its healing powers has been suppressed by those who work in religious and political circles and this deception has continued right up to the present day.

What would have happened to their religions if the public had been aware of the fact that much like Jesus himself, they too could heal the masses by simply using this plant? We have always been told that Jesus used the power of God to perform these miracles; so if the public had learned the truth, it probably would have a devastating effect on the belief systems they wanted us to accept.

Everything we were being told was designed to convince the public to continue believing the religious dogmas, which they were being fed and for us all to remain enslaved to the agendas of those who wished to control our existence. It appears "Thou Shalt Not Kill" was given little consideration by the individuals who brought this all about, for obviously it seems their only aim was to have more money and power at their disposal and they cared little or nothing about those who were being harmed.

For instance, it is widely rumored that hemp medicines are available to people who live and work in the Vatican, while most of us who live elsewhere have been denied the use of this substance. I have no idea how others will look at all this but after learning the truth, how could anyone dispute what I have stated?

The current restrictions against hemp's growing and use were not put into effect because this plant presented any real danger to the public. Instead, these laws were forced upon us by political graft and corruption so big money interests and religious organizations could enrich themselves, while we were left to suffer and die because they had successfully robbed us of our right to heal ourselves with this God given plant.

Look at what would take place if we were to be given the opportunity to grow hemp again, the same as our ancestors did, and with this new found knowledge about its healing virtues were able to heal ourselves. What do you think the reaction of the pharmaceutical industry and other big money interests would be if this were ever to come about? The drug companies and governments they control would do everything possible to stop this from occurring, for if they did not, all the lies they have told us in the past would be exposed. To prevent all the public outrage such a thing would cause, this is currently what is taking place and those who wish to keep us enslaved will stop at nothing to maintain the deception they have perpetrated.

Many large pharmaceutical companies which still exist today sold hemp-based medicines in the 1800's and early 1900's. Since these companies produced hemp-based medicines for decades, they had to know then what I have recently learned for myself about the healing virtues of this plant. If this were not the case, then why was the real essential oil from the hemp plant never made available to the public in an undiluted form?

At that time, drug companies produced many different plant extracts for medicinal use, so why would they not manufacture the concentrated extracts from what was then known to be the most medicinal plant in existence? Put simply, if they had no idea about the medical wonders this plant could produce, then it can only be said that drug companies of that era must have achieved new levels in the field of stupidity.

Hemp oil, if manufactured and used properly, is a cure-all that the pharmaceutical industry cannot patent and since hemp is a plant, no one should ever have this right. That is one of the main reasons why its use has been restricted. But there are also many other big money interests that would lose a great deal of money and business if we were all to start growing this plant on a large scale.

While still in Canada, I contacted the Liberals, the Conservatives, the Green Party, and the New Democratic Party about this situation. I provided them with evidence to back-up what I was saying and of course, I would have been happy to introduce them to the patients. Not one of these political parties would lift a finger to look into this issue and in most cases I did not even receive a reply.

In addition, I also contacted the RCMP along with the news media and many other organizations and public interest TV shows, but received little or no response for my efforts. We even took our concerns to the United Nations and they too refused to take any interest, as a matter of fact they did not even reply to our request that this should be looked into.

Why are all these supposedly intelligent individuals trying to avoid such a simple truth, when indeed their friends and loved ones are suffering also? If I am in some way wrong in what I have been saying, then I invite the system to come and prove it to us all publicly. If allowed, I would be happy to put on a public demonstration, concerning what this oil can really do medicinally so the truth can finally be exposed. This would provide the real facts to the Canadian public and everyone else in an irrefutable manner. It seems unbelievable that we have a law in Canada, which will not allow us to cure our own diseases with a natural herbal remedy but sadly, that is currently the case.

While much of the evidence for the effectiveness of hemp extracts comes in the form of reports from patients, it is important to realize that most doctors will refuse to support this medication's use because in a short time it would affect their incomes and positions. Many doctors have seen what this oil can do, but the medical system has done everything possible to keep the medical records of patients who used it hidden.

Untold numbers of people worldwide have now experienced what this simple oil has done for their health issues and you cannot stop word of mouth from traveling. The greatest researchers in this field of study are now for the most part even in agreement with the vast majority of what I have been telling the public about this medication's use over the last ten years.

In addition to all this evidence, there is no shortage of information which supports the use of this medication as well. Reports from many researchers and their published studies are available online, for instance at

"Granny Storm Crow's List" compilation of medical reports and studies about hemp. One can also simply go to PubMed or Google and enter cannabinoids and cancer, I think if anyone were to do so, it would satisfy all their scientific concerns.

At present, we are experiencing a cancer epidemic and there is no question that properly produced cannabis extracts are very effective in the treatment of all forms of this disease. The fact must also be made clear that this medication is of great benefit in healing or controlling all types of other medical conditions as well. So why are we not demanding this oil's free medicinal use? It should not be forgotten that for instance, penicillin was approved for use after only trying it on six patients and unlike hemp oil, which poses no danger, if the patient happens to be allergic to penicillin, it can bring about their death.

So when they began to use this substance for medical purposes, in reality they had much less experience and data than what is now currently available on the effectiveness and uses of hemp extracts. The results that patients have achieved with the use of this natural oil can be readily replicated by almost anyone who will take the time to produce and use this substance properly. To the best of my knowledge, I am not aware of any medication that is better suited to treat cancer and other serious conditions effectively. But more importantly, it can save lives while doing the patients no harm.

The topical application of hemp oil or tinctures, salves, balms, and creams that contain this substance helps to control or cure a vast array of skin conditions. Everything from unhealthy warts and moles to external skin disorders, which often were thought to be incurable can now be treated at home in a safe and effective manner.

Taken orally or in suppository form, the healing cannabinoids this oil contains tend to seek out and destroy cancer cells and while doing so, it resets your body to a state of good health. In addition, using devices, which were properly designed to fulfill this role, hemp oil can be vaporized to effectively treat many different types of lung conditions, including cancer. However, it is always a good idea to ingest the oil orally or in suppository form as well to receive the most benefits.

If one ingests high-grade cannabis extracts produced from strains which have strong pain killing effects, you will find that it can eliminate pain that even morphine and other dangerous toxic addictive pain medications cannot. From my experience, I can honestly say that I am not aware of a safer or more effective painkiller on this planet.

Much like any other powerful medication, if some individuals ingest too much, it can bring about undesirable side effects. Although the effects which this oil may produce do not pose a danger, there are those who do not enjoy becoming high from an overdose. Even though this medication is safe and most have no problems with its use, one should also take into consideration that there will be those who will experience difficulties.

That is the reason I instruct everyone to start out with very small doses, then increase the amount they are ingesting every four days. By doing so, it affords the person who is taking this substance the opportunity to build up their tolerance and many patients have reported that they did not feel as though they had become high during the treatment. If hemp oil is produced properly from very potent sedative strains of cannabis indica, or often when it is manufactured from some types of indica dominant sativa crosses, one will find that the effects of such oils will promote drowsiness and sleep, which are obviously an important part of the healing process.

Patients should be aware of the fact that this oil can also reduce their blood pressure, ocular pressure, and blood sugar levels. If individuals are taking medications to treat these issues, in most cases they should be able to reduce their need for the use of the drugs they are currently using very rapidly. I must inform patients who take blood pressure medication that once they start the oil, often their blood pressure issues will no longer require the use of pharmaceuticals and this also holds true for diabetics and those who suffer with glaucoma as well.

Please be aware that if oil is to be ingested to treat other conditions and it is taken along with blood pressure medications, it can in some cases drive the patient's blood pressure down too low. Although I do not know of anyone who experienced this who suffered any real harm, I still feel one should try to avoid this situation if at all possible. So check your blood pressure often and if pharmaceuticals are no longer required do not ingest them.

It may seem unbelievable to some individuals that they can discontinue the use of these prescribed substances. However, once one realizes the healing potential of this natural medicine, they soon come to understand that this amazing oil can replace the use of practically all pharmaceuticals.

For those of you who may find it inconceivable that our trusted medical establishment would ignore or even have disdain for the medicinal use of cannabis hemp, we must remind the reader that the history of medicine includes many examples of mule-like stubbornness, incompetence, mediocrity, greed, arrogance, and stupidity. Consider the case of a much-respected Hungarian physician named Dr. Ignas Semmelweis.

In 1847, this doctor was concerned about the high mortality rate of women giving birth in hospitals. So he instituted a procedure at one hospital, whereby doctors washed and disinfected their hands before delivering babies. Immediately, the mortality rate dropped from 30% to near zero. Seven other hospitals then decided to follow suit, by asking doctors to wash their hands before delivering a child and they were all able to achieve similar results.

Although the request Dr. Semmelweis asked other doctors to perform was simply based in common sense, the European medical establishment failed to recognize what he had accomplished. Afterwards, applications from the good doctor for further research funds were blocked and they then vilified and ostracized him, which ultimately caused the loss of the prestigious positions he had held at maternity hospitals. In America, the newly formed American Medical Association added insult to injury by threatening to revoke the license of any doctor caught washing their hands. Dr. Semmelweis was so distressed that women and children continued to die that he suffered a mental breakdown, which eventually led to his death in 1865.

Do not expect a doctor working within the system to buck the system. The penalty for doing so is just too great for them and most will not run the risk of having their license to practice medicine revoked. What your doctor prescribes is controlled by a large medical industry that makes its profits by supplying what they tell us are very costly medications and other so-called treatments like radiation, which fit into their general profit-making scheme of things. It is an industry that does not look favorably upon natural supplements or other treatments that they cannot patent and make huge amounts of money from for themselves.

In the near future, due to the impact, which cannabis extracts are about to have on the medical world, many of the current so-called conventional treatments used by doctors at present will then be viewed in much the same way that we today look at the old archaic medical practices of using mercury and bloodletting to cure illnesses.

The scope of uses this medicine encompasses is very wide and usually exceeds what any ordinary person who has not seen its effects for themselves can imagine. I always tell patients who come to seek out my advice about treatment with the oil that they don't have to believe a thing I am saying and I encourage everyone to simply prove it to themselves. All they have to do is acquire an ounce of high-quality indica bud and then, following my instructions, produce the essential oil.

If you have good bud to work with at your disposal, this amount of starting material should provide three to four milliliters of high-grade oil. All you have to do afterwards is find someone who is in need of treatment that is suffering from skin cancer, a severe burn or a diabetic ulcer etc. Then apply the oil topically and cover the area with a bandage. Re-apply the oil and a fresh bandage every three days and watch what happens. Now, you have seen for yourself what this oil can do and then you can start building your confidence with the use of this substance, just as I did.

Back in the early 1900s, a simple tactic called the big lie was employed to help enable corrupted governments in their quest to outlaw hemp. The wealthy that really control our political systems wanted this plant restricted for their own monetary reasons. In the hope of achieving their aims, they simply renamed cannabis hemp marijuana, then told the public imaginary horror stories about this new drug's terrible effects in their news media.

Although it is a proven fact that hemp was freely grown in America long before the United States came into being and that even after the US declared itself to be a country, farmers were allowed to pay their taxes with this plant. For monetary reasons, which I have already discussed, the growing and use of the cannabis hemp plant was suddenly deemed to be against the law in the 1930s.

One would think that it should have been impossible for the American government and many others worldwide to shove this nonsense down the throats of farmers, who had been growing this plant as a crop for hundreds of years. Nevertheless, the big lie worked its magic and the farmers simply rolled over and did what the government demanded. Now they could no longer grow one of their oldest and most important staples and even to the present day, they are still not allowed to do so.

Hitler's propaganda minister Joseph Goebbels also used the big lie method to sway the masses in Germany before and during the Second World War to help keep public sentiment behind their brand of insanity. Goebbels apparently felt that even if something is not true, all he had to do is state it often and loudly enough and soon, the public would accept his statements as being facts.

Unfortunately, propaganda of this nature is still in wide spread use today and recent events, which we have all witnessed, should be more than enough to prove this fact.

For instance, look into what we were told by our trusted officials concerning who was responsible for 9/11 and the consequences, which innocent nations had to face who in reality played no role in this event. This should make it more than obvious; the big lie method of spreading propaganda still has some merit. Since to date nothing has been done to bring the real criminals who perpetrated this crime to justice.

If those who are trying to deceive us can use such tactics and it seems to have the desired effect upon the public, could one not also bring the public the big truth in the same manner? To accept all the rubbish we have been told by those who are presently in control required that most of us reject our capacity for rational thought. In other words, we simply let them tell us that black is white and we all went along with their deceptions without question.

I prefer to believe that most individuals are a bit more in tune with reality than those who are in control would like. I think most of us do have a certain degree of common sense and in a short while, we may begin to utilize our thinking capacities to make life on this planet better for everyone.

This book is based on articles and interviews, written by me, which were reviewed in the fall of 2012. We are happy to announce that Max Igan has also graciously supplied a chapter, which I am sure readers will find very informative and we have tried to devote enough space, so many questions and answers could be addressed as well. As the reader will notice, some of the information inevitably repeats in several parts of this book. In such cases, please remember that while repetition may not be the mother of wisdom, it certainly is the mother of knowing.

Before you begin to read this book, there is something I would like to make clear to everyone. No matter how often I use the term cure-all, many people still do not seem to be able to understand that indeed I am saying this medication is effective in the treatment of every disease which I know of that exists. Over the years, I have provided this oil to vast numbers of people who were afflicted with all types of medical difficulties. This allowed me to see for myself what this natural healing substance was capable of doing.

After dealing with thousands of individuals who were suffering with serious medical issues, I can only report that the success rate of this medication literally defies description. So if anything can help with your health problems, I strongly suspect that it will be the essential oil of the cannabis hemp plant.

No matter who you are, it is now virtually impossible to avoid all the toxins that we are exposed to in our day to day lives. Therefore, I feel that we should all consider taking a full sixty-gram treatment of oil over the period of two or three months to detoxify ourselves before health problems can arise. After this has been accomplished, maintenance doses, which in total equal 1 to 2 grams per month, should be ingested. Doing what I am suggesting can not only rectify your health in most cases, it will also protect those who follow my instructions from medical issues which can be avoided in the future.

The earth upon which we dwell is becoming more toxic every day. In addition, to maintain the profit margins of the big drug companies, our misguided medical systems do not hesitate to fill our children full of chemicals and poisons whenever possible. Since it is more than obvious that what I am stating is true, it only seems logical to me that in many cases children who have been exposed to dangerous medical toxins and other harmful substances, which seem to be everywhere these days, also need to be detoxified and they should all be taking at least maintenance doses of this oil to remain in good health.

Most individuals do not take the time to realize that the jobs they are presently doing, and many of the professions they have chosen to follow, are for the most part doing harm to this earth and their own loved ones. No matter what field of endeavor you chose to follow these days, it seems that most are directly or indirectly poisoning our planet, which in turn is affecting the well-being of us all.

One would think that by this stage of our evolution, the human race should be doing everything possible to make this world a better place, but sadly, as yet, this has not come to pass. I know what I am stating paints a horrible picture of our way of life, but show me any sensible person that can present a valid argument, which disproves what I am saying. This is the world that we have all played a role in creating. Now it is up to those who are rational among us to show humanity that indeed we can maintain ourselves in a much more sensible and sustainable manner.

Better health and living conditions are something we can easily achieve. All we have to do is awaken ourselves to the fact that if things are going to change, we are the ones who must bring it about. Enough with wasting our time asking corrupted government officials to solve our problems. I think it is high time that we as humans begin to stand on our own two feet and learn to deal with our problems and concerns in a much more sensible and honest way.

Once we discover that indeed we do have the ability to make things better for everyone, we may just find the road to paradise, for which we have all been longing.

CHAPTER 1

HEMP: THE MOST MEDICINAL PLANT ON EARTH IN ACTION

HOW IT ALL STARTED

How did you come to discover how to cure cancer and many other illnesses with hemp?

I consider myself just one of many who have found a way to cure cancer and I certainly was not the first one to produce an essential oil from the cannabis plant. A radio broadcast told me that THC (tetrahydrocannabinol) kills cancer cells way back in the 1970's, so I do not claim that it was me who found the cure. Still, it does appear that I am the first to supply this medication to vast numbers of patients to treat their cancers and other conditions in a more effective and sensible way.

In addition, I continued to report my findings openly to the general public after the government and all they control turned their backs on this issue. Since this plant has been used in medicine for thousands of years, I really do not think that anyone can make the claim that they alone discovered its true medical values.

The only thing that I can really claim is that I discovered the proper way to produce and use this substance and I developed and published a protocol to make it more simple for patients to enjoy its use. As often as I could, I provided the medicine free of charge and I openly reported my findings to anyone who would listen, expecting that sooner or later someone would do something about it.

How did you find out about THC being effective to treat cancer?
In 1972, I watched my 25-year-old cousin die a horrible death from cancer. About three years later, I heard a report on our local radio station CKDH in Amherst, Nova Scotia. The announcer was laughing like a fool when he gave the report, so I did not know whether to take the report seriously. He stated that THC (the active ingredient in marijuana) has been found to kill cancer cells.

After this report, I heard nothing more on this subject, so I assumed it must have been some kind of joke. About thirty years later, I found out that the report was true and it was from the Medical School of Virginia study done in the mid-1970's.

In 1997, I suffered a head injury that left me with post-concussion syndrome. Post-concussion syndrome can affect people in different ways and many wind up with severe migraines and other problems. The injury I sustained left me with what can only be termed as migraine noise. It's like having a tuning fork gone mad in your head that you cannot silence and this in turn can cause blood pressure issues and other medical problems. If this condition persists and you cannot find a way to deal with it, the noise takes over your life and you get very little rest.

The chemicals the medical system gave me did nothing for my condition but make me worse with their side effects. Then in 1998, I saw an episode of The Nature of Things entitled "Reefer Madness II." Dr. David Suzuki interviewed people who were smoking hemp for their medical conditions and the results were amazing. After watching the show, I purchased some hemp to see if it would help my condition.

When I smoked hemp for my condition, it relaxed me and allowed me to get more sleep. Smoking this substance did not take the noise in my head away but it did make the condition much easier to live with. I asked many doctors for a prescription for hemp but was refused. They would use excuses like "it's still under study" and "hemp is bad for the lungs" or some other such nonsense.

In 1999, I asked my family doctor what he thought about me producing the essential oil from the hemp plant and ingesting it as a medication as opposed to smoking the plant material. He said ingesting the oil would be much more medicinal, but still would not provide me with a prescription.

By 2001, the medical system had written me off. I was told by my doctor that they had tried every medication at their disposal but none of them helped me, so I was now on my own. My family doctor knew very well that the only medication which gave me any relief was hemp. He also knew that I would be classified as a criminal if I were caught using hemp for my condition, but still he would provide no prescription, the same as all the other doctors I had asked.

Can you imagine I worked 32 years for the system and never had a drug charge in my life? Now, due to my need for this medication to treat my condition, suddenly I am now a criminal because they would not give me the legal right to use this medicine. Needless to say, all of this left a very bad taste in my mouth.

How long did it take to cure your skin cancer?

In late 2002, my doctor examined three areas on my body, which he suspected were skin cancer. One was close to my right eye, another was on my left cheek, and there was another area on my chest. In January 2003, I went in to have the cancer close to my right eye removed. I was then to go in at a later date and have the other two areas taken care of.

About a week after the surgery, I was examining the area where they had removed the cancer, when suddenly the report I had heard on the radio almost 30 years before popped back into my mind. The report had stated that THC kills cancer cells. I knew the oil I produced was full of THC, so I thought, "Why not put some oil on the other two cancers and see what happens?" I applied the oil, covered the affected areas with a bandage and left them in place four days. During this time, I felt nothing, so I assumed that the oil was not working.

Imagine my surprise after removing the bandages and seeing nothing but pink skin – the cancer was gone! Within seven weeks, the cancer close to my right eye that they had removed surgically returned. I applied the oil and a bandage to this area as well and in four days, it too was completely healed. Since there was already quite a bit of THC in my body, it only took four days to cure my skin cancer when I applied the oil topically. I performed these treatments on myself in the winter of 2003.

I have never applied oil to these areas again and the cancer has never returned, so just from my experience alone, I believe I have every right to say that hemp oil cured my cancer. It has certainly exceeded the five-year limit without returning, which is used as a measure by the medical system.

CHAPTER 2

HOW TO MAKE THE MEDICINE

All the information about how to produce the oil along with the dosage instructions are available on my website www.phoenixtears.ca or the public can view our documentary '**Run from the Cure**' (which is available on our YouTube channel www.youtube.com/user/RickSimpsonOilCure) which should answer any questions regarding producing your own oil. Also, on our publishing company's YouTube channel: https://www.youtube.com/c/simpsonramadur there is step-by-step video guide available titled '**Making Cannabis Oil with Rick Simpson**'.

Caution: I recommend that people grow their own cannabis strains, either in a small indoor grow system or outdoors. Growing it yourself will eliminate the high cost associated with buying hemp from drug dealers to suite you medical needs. The cost can vary greatly from dealer to dealer and so can the quality of the hemp they are offering, so at present I think growing your own is the best option.

Oils that drug dealers sell can have many contaminants and often little THC. From my experience, most hemp oil available on the street should be avoided for medicinal use.

At present, it is best to make your own oil or have someone you trust produce the substance for you to assure that a very pure, high quality oil is produced. The importance of the quality of the oil cannot be overemphasized and bud from the best medicinal strains are required in its production, so I recommend that patients always try to produce the finest oil possible to avoid disappointment.

Is the hemp oil you speak about the same as hemp seed oil?

No. This oil that my name has become connected with is a purified decarboxylated extract or essential oil, if you wish, produced from the bud material of medicinal varieties of the cannabis hemp plant. Hemp seed oil is an entirely different substance, but first I will explain more about the oil from the plant itself.

I always recommend high-grade oils for internal use in the treatment of serious conditions. A high-grade extract should contain THC levels in the range of 80-90% and produce an extremely sedative, yet euphoric effect when ingested. The higher the quality of the oil, the more pronounced will be its healing effects.

What I consider to be low grade extracts are basically any extracts that do not meet these specifications, which causes them to have a reduced healing effect. Most other methods of producing these oils do not meet the criteria I have put in place and that is why I always insist that people follow the instructions that I have provided. This will present the patient with the best chance of recovery and since so many have used my method successfully, I don't think it should be ignored in favor of other methods which as yet have not proven themselves.

Lower-grade oils produced from leaves and cuttings can be used for the treatment of many less serious issues like skin conditions, which often may be healed without the use of oils produced from high-grade bud. Even if ingested internally, some lower grade oils could have a positive effect on many conditions. But knowing what I know about the differences in the healing qualities of these oils, I could not honestly recommend the use of such oils in the treatment of serious conditions and I would consider supplying them as little more than an experiment with the patient's life.

So look for the best starting material available and always produce an oil of the highest possible quality. If your life was on the line, I think it would only be fair to assume that you would want the best, so please try to provide others with the same.

When I started supplying this oil, I did not know what to call it other than what it was, hemp oil, but it seems my use of this term has caused many to misunderstand. Health food stores sell oil made from hemp seeds that is often mislabeled as hemp oil. What they really are selling is cold-pressed hemp seed oil and that is what should be on their label. Although seed oil is very beneficial and is indeed a wonderful source of nutrition, it does not contain enough THC and other cannabinoids to have the desired effect on cancer and other serious illnesses.

Hemp seeds and hemp seed oil have been a part of human and animal diets for thousands of years, and I encourage everyone to include this substance in their diet as well. But do not expect hemp seed oil to have the same healing effects as the concentrated extract from the plant itself. Although hemp oil and hemp seed oil are two different substances, hemp seed oil is beneficial for cardiovascular problems and it is also useful to improve our circulatory system.

When finished properly, the oil I produce is a thick grease-like substance, while hemp seed oil will run freely at room temperature, so there is really no resemblance between the two.

Are hemp and marijuana the same?

The word marijuana is one of over four hundred slang terms used worldwide to describe the cannabis hemp and/or hemp plant. I use the term hemp because that is what farmers throughout history have called it and many varieties that were grown long ago would now be called marijuana due to their higher resin content.

Put simply, governments and their masters, the power elite, started using the word marijuana to describe varieties of hemp that contained larger amounts of medicinal resins. They also used the dreaded M-word to scare the public into believing that hemp was harmful and not fit to be used as a medicine. Of course, none of this had any basis in fact and it was only designed to keep the profit margins of drug companies and others at extremely high levels. So in reality marijuana was simply a word they used as a scare tactic to keep the public from using hemp both recreationally and medicinally.

WHAT STRAIN OR STRAINS SHOULD I USE TO MAKE THE OIL?

This is a rather hard question to answer, since in reality we are all at the mercy of the seed merchants, for they are the ones who have the final say in what we are growing.

The trouble is if you were to order a strain like *White Widow* from five different seed suppliers, when you grew them, you would likely end up growing five entirely different types of cannabis. The type of *White Widow* that I was growing back in Canada had a very heavy sedative effect like a good indica variety and it was one of the best painkillers I have ever encountered. But if I tried to order the same seeds from the company I originally purchased them from, today they would likely send me seeds with entirely different medicinal values.

The *White Widow* I have seen in Europe is much more energizing than what I was growing in Canada, so it seems seeds available here must be more sativa dominant. Unfortunately, for the most part, it did not have the medicinal values that I am looking for to produce the heavy sleepy effect like the *White Widow* I was growing back in Canada.

Some strains are better for pain relief, while others will be more effective to control blood sugar levels for diabetics or to lower ocular pressure for those suffering from glaucoma. We need a good ongoing steady supply of seeds that have known medicinal values so an ordinary person will know what they are growing. All we need is the freedom to grow the most medicinal strains on earth, then using a simple process of elimination, we could determine which strains produce the best oil to treat different medical conditions.

After this is done, a stable supply of these seeds could be made available to the public and they then could grow strains that suit their medical needs. But until that day comes, I cannot really recommend a particular strain or seed vendor and say that "this is the one for you" and has "guaranteed effects".

Some seed companies do have information available about the medicinal values of the strains they are selling. So it would be a good idea to look this information over before making your purchase.

What strains should patients look for then?

At this time, all I can do is instruct the public to order strong sedative indica varieties or highly dominant indica crosses which have 20% THC or more to produce their oil. In addition, people are always asking me where they can get seeds and this can be a real problem for those who live in some countries that don't allow them to be sold. If you go on the Internet and you will find many seed companies that will supply cannabis seeds and some ship worldwide. (Tip: Google the words marijuana seeds worldwide and you will see a selection of online shops that might cater your needs).

What does one have to watch for when choosing or purchasing plants for producing the oil?

For people who have no experience with hemp, they must be careful, since many growers and dealers will simply try to sell you whatever they have. For those who have never smoked hemp, I suggest they take someone with experience along when they make their purchase.

You cannot always go by look and smell to determine the potency of cannabis. I have seen buds that glistened with resin and smelled beautifully but they lacked the potency to produce good medication. So it's best to find out how potent the material is before you purchase a large quantity.

When someone brings a pound to produce the medicine, I first test its effects on myself. I cut up a little bit of bud and roll a joint with it. If the hemp is good, by the time I have smoked half the joint, I feel its effects. What I look for is a heavy sleepy sensation that makes you want to go lay down. If I am smoking a good indica or an indica dominant sativa cross which is only about 10% sativa, usually such varieties will exhibit these effects.

I have found that practically all hemp varieties which produce this heavy, sleepy feeling are very medicinal. These are the varieties I used with such great success when producing oils to treat cancer and other serious internal problems.

Why do you recommend that people make the oil from a pound or more of the starting material? Could they produce it from say an ounce of dried hemp?'

Yes, of course, the oil can be produced in smaller amounts as well. An ounce of good dry hemp bud should produce 3 to 4 grams of high-grade oil and only about 16 fluid ounces of solvent would be required to do the two washes.

But there are reasons I suggest that patients produce the oil from a pound if possible and they involve putting the patient at ease with its use. I feel even those who are relatively healthy should ingest a full 60 gram treatment to detoxify their bodies and bring them back to a state of good health. To produce this much oil usually requires about a pound of bud and I think it is somewhat easier on the patient if they do not try to produce oils from many different varieties.

Each strain produces oils with different effects so if the patient is switching from one strain to another, they never know what to expect.

For those who are at ease with this medication's use, switching oils presents little or no problems. But for patients who are experiencing its effects for the first time, I think it's best if they are only ingesting one type of oil.

How strong and potent are the plants you use for making the oil?

I always make the medicine from the strongest and most sedative material available to me and often the strains I work with produce a euphoric effect as well. Oils produced from strains with these traits have very pleasant effects and patients tend to enjoy taking them.

Many pot smokers in the region I come from often used to complain that I buy up all the good hemp for medicine and leave nothing for those who wish to smoke. I don't pay much attention to this, since I consider saving lives to be far more important than the recreational needs of those who are not ill.

I am always looking for strains that exhibit heavy resin content and the proper medicinal values. Much of the material I use to produce the medicine comes from varieties, which are supposed to be in the 20% THC range. Of course, if these strains actually contained that much THC, one pound would produce 90 to 100 grams of oil, but usually that is not the case. There are some who actually do grow medicinal hemp which has a very high resin content, but take it from me, hemp of this quality can often be very expensive and hard to find.

Most of the bud material which was available to me from other growers would produce around 60 grams of high-grade oil per dry pound; so no doubt the quality could have been better. But in reality, I had very little choice in the matter, since if I was to attempt to save the lives of patients, I had to use what was available. What people really need to know is that each strain will vary in the amount of oil it produces and these oils will vary in medicinal values as well.

In addition, the methods used to grow cannabis have a lot to do with how much THC is present in the dry bud material. The strain being grown may be capable of producing buds which can contain 20% THC or even more but many growers do not have the skills or facilities needed to achieve this. I have worked with strains that produced 90 grams of oil out of one dry pound of bud and sometimes even a bit more. But unfortunately, hemp of this quality is quite rare, so if you can extract 60 grams of good oil from a dry pound of hemp bud, be happy. Always look for the most potent hemp possible when purchasing the starting material; someone's life may depend on it.

Why are maintenance doses so important?

Everyone should be taking maintenance doses to keep their bodies detoxified and in a state of good health. All that is required is 1 to 2 grams of oil a month, just ingest a drop or two at night about an hour before bedtime. This will give you a good night's sleep and will provide protection from the toxins we are exposed to and in addition it will act to prevent diseases from occurring as well.

The oil works with your body to keep you healthy and to provide protection from a wide variety of health issues. I would not allow a child of mine to take these vaccines and shots which people like Bill Gates are trying to shove down our throats. If I want to protect my children from such things as the flu, I will put my trust in properly produced hemp oil, since I know it is effective and will cause no harm.

Are there any strains that are not effective against cancer?

Luckily for us, if the oil is properly produced from sedative varieties, it does seem to work very well in the treatment of all types of cancer. As I have mentioned already, I usually produce this oil using strong indica varieties but indica dominant sativa crosses can often produce excellent results also if the sativa content is very low. Therefore, I do not like to work with any strain which is more than 10% sativa and if possible I prefer to produce extracts from pure indica varieties. Although, I have worked with a great number of indica varieties and have achieved amazing success with their use, I still cannot say with any certainty that each and every indica strain would be effective in the treatment of cancer, this is something we will have to learn as the research goes on.

SATIVA VERSUS INDICA

What is the main difference between cannabis sativa and cannabis indica in treatment?

I do not like to see anyone ingesting sativa oil to treat cancer and other serious conditions. There is certainly a possibility that oil made from a good sativa could cure cancer but the energizing effect of this oil is not conducive to healing. Certainly, I would not hesitate to treat skin cancer externally with such an oil but ingesting oils from sativa varieties can badly affect the patient's sleeping patterns. I also consider such oils to be very effective in the treatment of people suffering from depression. In some cases, those who suffer from depression could benefit if they were to take a small dose of this oil when they get out of bed. This would energize them and lift their spirits, but if too much is taken, some strong sativa oils can be far too energizing and most people do not like this effect.

Although extracts produced from sativas can be beneficial in some situations, for the most part I try to avoid their use. Often these oils are far too energizing and I do not want to see someone with terminal cancer or other serious conditions out trying to paint the barn. Some patients do not handle the effects of energizing oils well, which often can make them very restless and cause anxiety. From my experience, the patient will respond much better if the oil is produced from sedative strains with traits like those that I have mentioned.

The extra sleep the patient will experience is very refreshing and logically, a well-rested patient will heal better than one who is experiencing sleeping difficulties. For internal use to treat most medical conditions, I strongly suggest that indica strains or indica dominant sativa crosses be used. Indicas relax a person and provide them with more rest, sleep and peace of mind.

I have also found that oils produced from pure indicas or indica dominant strains are effective in treating depression and other health related issues. From my perspective, oils produced form good indica strains are more medicinally desirable than most oils produced from sativa.

How would you describe the ideal oil that would produce the most enjoyable experience to patients?

After working with extracts from many indica varieties and mixtures of these extracts, which have been combined with others to produce the desired effects. In my estimation to provide the patient with the most enjoyable experience the extract should be highly sedative with slightly euphoric effects. If the patient has not yet built up their tolerance for this medication within an hour after ingesting their dosage they should begin to experience a pleasant euphoric sensation. Then a few minutes later the highly sedative nature of this medication will cause the patient to begin to get the sleep and rest they require to heal properly. The length of time needed for these effects to be felt by the patient will vary from one extract to another and some can take much longer before these effects become noticeable. But from my experience the highest quality extracts will usually produce these effects in an hour or less.

The patient can take their dosage at home but if the oil were allowed, in some situations I think this could be performed much better in a hospital setting. Unless the patient is close to death, I tell them to follow our dosage instructions, but if their life is in danger I recommend that they take this medication as quickly as possible.

Many who have smoked cannabis in the past have no fear of this substance and I have seen some people with terminal cancer cure their condition in a month. In reality, it's up to the patient themselves as to how quickly this medicine is taken, but in my opinion the faster the better. Once it becomes public knowledge how safe these extracts are to ingest, I expect that more will try to ingest it in a faster manner.

What do patients need to know to grow hemp?

For anyone new to growing cannabis, a good book or video on the subject is a necessity. Just go to one of the cannabis publications online or buy one of these publications at a local store where you live. Usually these magazines will tell you where good books are available on the subject. My personal favorite is *The Indoor Outdoor Medicinal Growers Bible* by Jorge Cervantes. In addition, Ed Rosenthal and many others have excellent books on the subject available as well.

For those who would like to learn more about hemp and its many uses, I strongly suggest they read Jack Herer's book, *"The Emperor Wears No Clothes"* or watch Jack's video *"Emperor of Hemp"*.

After the journey of discovery that this plant has taken me on, no matter what your medical problem, I feel if this medication will not help you, then I think it is highly unlikely that you can find anything that will. I have good reason to call this wonder of nature the plant with a thousand different medicinal profiles for once you experience the medical effects oils produced from different strains can have, you will understand exactly what I mean.

OUTDOOR VERSUS INDOOR

Are there differences between oils from indoor and outdoor plants?

I have produced the oil from hemp that was grown both indoors and out-doors with good results but I really prefer to work with cannabis that was grown outdoors, since on average high quality hemp grown outside in a good growing season can be more potent and often produces more resin. I attribute this mostly to the sun, for I do not believe that most indoor lighting systems can compete with this source of light. Also, there are other stresses and factors in nature which can affect the potency of the strain being grown that plants grown indoors do not encounter.

Hemp that is grown indoors of course can be very potent and will produce good medicine but there are many drawbacks involved with in-door growing. Plants that are grown inside are usually much smaller in stature than those grown outside. Also, with indoor setups, problems arise concerning smell, air movement, infestations, and heat. Indoor grow sys-tems usually produce a great quantity of excess heat and often infestations and plant growth are controlled with the use of chemicals.

I cannot say that I have encountered any problems producing medicine from indoor crops; so if you do not have an alternative, this is a good way to supply yourself. For those who do not live in a rural setting, I suggest they build or buy a small indoor growing system from which they can supply the medicinal needs of their whole family. Currently there are many different types of indoor grow chambers available or if you like you can always build your own. Still, from my perspective, there is only one way to grow hemp properly and that is in the great outdoors. Open ground with good drainage and a proper pH is what's required. This along with lots of sunshine, horse manure, and abundant quantities of water can pro-duce an amazing crop.

I have not noticed any differences in the hemp oil produced from in-door or outdoor plants other than the fact that indoor plants seem to be slightly less potent. But there could be several reasons as to why this oc-curred and possibly, under the proper conditions, indoor plants might be just as strong as those grown outdoors.

The most potent oils I have ever produced in Canada came from out-door plants. Indoor plants may produce slightly less potent oils but they are still highly effective as a medication. So, at the present time, I would work with the most potent sedative bud you can get, no matter if it comes from indoor or outdoor.

type of artificial light do you get best results with?

.e achieved the best results indoor using a combination of high-pres-
.e lights. We used a 1000-Watt high-pressure sodium and 1000-Watt
..etal halide in the same grow chamber to produce the largest buds I have
ever grown inside. Although I have never used 600-Watt high-pressure
sodium's in an indoor growing system, from what I can gather, such bulbs
are the most efficient because they put out the most lumens per watt. The
main problem with high-pressure lighting systems is the heat they produce
and the power they consume, so I have looked into other forms of lighting
to help solve these issues.

Standard 4-foot cool white florescent bulbs will grow cannabis quite
effectively in the vegetative state; but for budding I would recommend
much more light intensity. Today there are many forms of high intensity
LED and compact fluorescent fixtures available that growers have told
me achieve good results. This type of lighting produces very little heat, has
low power consumption, and these fixtures have a long life expectancy.

Over the last few years, the cost of these different forms of lighting
has dropped dramatically, so these fixtures are now in a price range many
growers can afford. To anyone new to the art of indoor growing, I believe
this form of lighting in conjunction with the use of fluorescent fixtures is
a good way to start out and can eliminate many of the problems associated
with high-pressure lighting systems.

Although LED and fluorescent fixtures can grow a nice indoor crop,
the light source I am the most excited about is plasma lighting. From what
I understand, it is very energy-efficient with low heat output and the
amount of light that just one 1000-Watt bulb can give off is almost beyond
comprehension. Just the use of one such bulb can eliminate the need of
using many 1000-Watt high pressure sodiums. For larger growers, this can
help solve their heat problems and lower their energy and wiring costs
dramatically. At present, such lighting is quite expensive but, like LED
fixtures, the price will soon come down.

I think a plasma or LED fixture in the same light spectrum as our sun
in your grow room would be a good investment for most serious growers.
In a short time, I expect to see LED and plasma fixtures change the face
of indoor growing forever and make things much less complicated for all
who are involved in growing the cannabis hemp plant.

MY PROCESS OF PRODUCING HEMP OIL

I usually work with a pound or more of quality bud from very potent pure medicinal indica varieties or indica dominant sativa crosses which contain a very low percentage of sativa. An ounce of good bud will usually produce 3 to 4 grams of high-grade oil and the amount of oil produced will vary from strain to strain. You are never exactly sure how much oil you will produce until you have processed the material you are working with. On average, a pound of good bud will usually produce about 60 grams of high-grade extracts and sometimes you may even get substantially more from some varieties.

Many seem to believe the oil must be amber and that you should be able to see through it. Often the oils I produced did exhibit these traits but not always. The color and texture of the oil you are producing depends a great deal on the strain, method, and solvent that you are using to produce the oil. Don't be concerned if the oil you produce happens to be darker in color, this does not mean that such an oil is not a potent medicine. Indeed, some of the strongest oils I have ever produced were dark in color, but they still had the desired medicinal effects.

I think these instructions should make producing these extracts quite easy for anyone, but before you start, make sure that you have everything you will need to do it properly. All one requires is the starting material, solvent, a length of wood, two plastic buckets, a few small containers with funnels and coffee filters, an electric rice cooker, a fan, a stainless steel measuring cup, a coffee warmer, and syringes.

The process I am about to describe involves washing the starting material twice with a good solvent such as pure light naphtha or 99% isopropyl alcohol to remove the available resin from the plant material. Naphtha has proven itself to be a very good solvent to produce these extracts and it is also quite cheap to purchase when compared to the cost of other solvents. It comes in different forms and under different names but the solvent I used is called light naphtha in Canada and in Europe it is often called benzin(e). If you go to a fuel supplier, you should not have too much trouble tracking some down (CAS: CAS 64742-49-0).

Naphtha has many industrial uses, and is often used to degrease engine parts etc., so I'm sure you should have little trouble finding what you need. Just to give you an idea of its many uses, it is the same substance used to fuel Coleman lamps and stoves. But, unfortunately, rust inhibitors are added to Coleman fuel, so I do not recommend that this fuel be used to produce oil.

Butane can produce oil but I do not recommend its use as a solvent to produce this medication, since it is very volatile and would require the use of expensive equipment to neutralize the danger. In addition, using butane to produce the oil does not decarboxylate the finished product and so oils produced in this manner would be less effective for medicinal use unless the extra time is taken to decarboxylate them properly.

The only solvents that I have direct experience with so far are ether, naphtha, and isopropyl alcohol. Ether is my personal favorite and it is a very effective solvent but it is expensive and can be quite hard to get. I think the use of ether is better suited for closed distilling devices, since it is very volatile and its fumes make it dangerous to work with. Both ether and naphtha are more selective solvents in nature, which means alcohol is not quite as effective as a solvent but still it does work well. Alcohol will dissolve more chlorophyll from the starting material and due to this, oils produced with alcohol will usually be more noticeably dark in color.

For a solvent to be most effective, it should be 100% pure, and 100% pure alcohol is expensive and can be quite hard to find. Naphtha on the other hand is quite cheap to acquire and is usually not too hard to locate. Next to the use of ether, naphtha is my solvent of choice.

All these solvents including alcohol are poisonous in nature but if you follow these instructions, solvent residue in the finished oil is not a concern. After the finished product cools to room temperature, it is a thick grease-like substance rather than an oil and it is about as anti-poisonous as you can get. Even if there was a slight trace of solvent residue remaining, the oil itself would act upon it to neutralize any harmful poisonous effect. In essence, all you are doing is washing the medicinal resins off the bud material. Then after the solvent oil mix has been filtered and the solvent has been boiled off, you are left with the resins in their most medicinal form.

For best results, the starting material must be as dry as possible. Be sure where you are working is well-ventilated and there are no sparks, open flames, or red-hot elements in the area. Place the starting material in a container of good depth to prevent the oil solvent mix from splashing out during the washing process. Then dampen the bud with the solvent being used and the bud material is then crushed using a length of wood such as a piece of 2×2.

After it has been crushed, add more solvent until the material is completely immersed in the solvent. Work the bud material for about three minutes with the length of wood you used to crush it. Then slowly pour the solvent oil mix off into another clean container, leaving the starting material in the original container, so it can be washed for the second time.

Again add fresh solvent to the starting material until it is once more immersed in the solvent, and then work it for three more minutes with the length of wood you have been using. Then, pour the solvent oil mix into the same container that is holding the solvent oil mix from the first wash you did. Trying to do a third wash on the plant material produces very little oil and it would be of less benefit as a medicine. The first wash dissolves 70 to 80% of the available resin off the starting material; the second wash then removes whatever resin that is of benefit which remains.

Extracts produced from the first wash are the most potent medicinally but if high-grade starting material is used, oil from the second wash also has benefits. If for some reason you have to work with material which is not as potent as it should be, it is best to use the oil from the first wash only for internal use and then start to grow or look for starting material that is of better quality. Remember, quality is more important than quantity and the better the starting material, the better the medicine.

Use something such as clean water containers with a small opening at the top and insert funnels into the openings, then put large coffee filters in the funnels. Pour the solvent oil mix from the first and second washes into the coffee filters and allow the solvent oil mix to drain through the filters to remove any unwanted plant material. The more funnels and containers you use, the faster it will be filtered. Once the solvent oil mix has been filtered, it is now ready to have the solvent boiled off.

If you do not already own one, you can purchase an inexpensive large rice cooker with an open top that has both high and low heat settings to boil the solvent off the oil. Make sure that the rice cooker is set up in a well-ventilated area and place a fan nearby to blow away the fumes as the solvent boils off. This will prevent the fumes from condensing and posing a danger.

Rice cookers are designed so they do not burn the rice as it cooks. The temperature sensors that are built in will automatically switch the cooker back on the low heat setting if the temperature within the cooker begins to get too high. When producing oil, if the temperature gets a little over

300°F (148°C), it will begin to vaporize THC and other cannabinoids off the oil and of course you do not want this to occur.

If a rice cooker is working properly, it will automatically come off the high heat setting at roughly 230°F (110°C), which is above the temperature where decarboxylation is said to occur and is well below the point that cannabinoids will vaporize. This is why I strongly recommend the use of a rice cooker to those who have never produced oil before, since their use eliminates any danger of harming the oil produced. Plus the resulting oil is decarboxylated, which is also important so it can achieve its full medicinal potential.

I suggest that people should not try to use crock-pots and similar appliances to produce oil. When I first tried to produce the oil, I used a crock-pot and since I did not know how much heat these devices can generate, the oil overheated and was ruined. So I think it's only sensible that a beginner should start out by using a rice cooker and follow our instructions carefully since it could save them a lot of grief.

A distilling device can also be used to produce this medication and reclaim the solvent that is being used. This method really does make more sense than using a rice cooker, but stills that are designed to boil off solvents safely are expensive and most people do not know how to operate one of these devices properly. If one is available, I prefer to use a still myself, but in some countries owning a still is against the law. If one is serious and wants to produce large amounts of oil, look into distilling and educate yourself in the proper use of this equipment.

Always make sure there are no sparks, open flames, or red-hot elements in the area while you are filling the rice cooker or boiling the solvent off, because the fumes produced from these solvents are very flammable. I have used this same process thousands of times and have never had a mishap, but for your own safety, please follow the instructions and make sure the area is well-ventilated. I also caution you to avoid breathing in the toxic fumes that solvents produce, since they can have unpleasant effects on anyone nearby.

Make sure that the fan is running and produces enough airflow to blow away the fumes, then fill the rice cooker until it is about three quarters full. This allows room for the solvent oil mix to boil off without spilling over. Put the rice cooker on its high heat setting and begin boiling the solvent off. Never attempt to do this without the use of a fan, since the fumes could condense and if they come in contact with the heating element, it might cause a fire.

As the level in the rice cooker drops, continue to carefully add the solvent-oil mix you have remaining until you have nothing left. When the level in the rice cooker comes down for the last time and has been reduced to about two inches of solvent oil mix remaining, add about 10 to 12 drops of water to the solvent oil mix that remains. This small amount of water allows the remaining solvent to boil off the oil which is in the cooker more readily. In addition since the solvent boils off at a much lower temperature than water. The tiny particles of water which remain after the solvent has been boiled off, will then turn into steam and as the steam rises through the oil to escape, it is actually washing the oil to remove most or all of any solvent residue which the oil still might contain.

When there is very little remaining in the cooker, I usually put on a pair of gloves and then pick up the cooker and begin swirling its contents. This is done with the airflow from the fan still taking the fumes away and it may speed up the finishing process slightly. In a short time, the cooker automatically kicks off its high heat setting and then goes to low heat.

As the last of the solvent is being boiled off, you will hear a crackling sound from the oil that is left in the cooker and you will usually see quite a bit of bubbling still taking place in the oil that remains. Also, you will notice what looks like a small amount of smoke coming off the oil in the rice cooker, but don't be concerned as this is just steam produced from the few drops of water that you added.

After the rice cooker has automatically switched to its low-heat setting, I usually let it cool until it can be switched to the high-heat setting again. After the cooker has automatically switched itself to the low-heat setting for the second time, I then take the inner pot out of the cooker and pour its contents into a stainless steel measuring cup. In some cases you will find that the extract is actually finished and ready for use after the rice cooker has automatically gone back to its low heat setting for the second time. If there is little or no bubbling activity often the extracts can be drawn into the plastic syringes without even taking the extract out of the pot.

There will be a small amount of oil remaining in the pot that you will find almost impossible to get out unless you use something like dry bread to absorb the oil while it is still warm. Then, small amounts of this bread can be eaten as a medicine, but remember it can sometimes take an hour or more before you feel its effects. So be careful how much bread like this you consume, because even a very small amount may put you to sleep for quite a few hours just the same as the raw oil will do itself. Another good way to clean up whatever oil remains in the pot is to wash the pot out with a small amount of alcohol to produce a hemp oil tincture. A tincture such as this can be very effective in the treatment of skin conditions and just a little can go a long way, which can save you money. In addition, dry tobacco can also be used to remove the oil which remains in the pot as well and I have always referred to what results as being happy tobacco. It has now been proven that even the smoking aspects of cannabis can have beneficial medical effects. So for those who already smoke tobacco adding cannabinoids in the form of these extracts to the tobacco they are smoking would certainly do them no harm.

Since I often like to mix oil from several strains anyway, I usually simply leave the remaining oil in the pot until next time. By mixing oils from different strains, you receive the medicinal benefits from all these different types of oil and I have found such oils to be effective in the treatment of practically everything. If you have many different varieties of good medicinal hemp at your disposal, I think mixing the oils is a good idea. But if you do not, I believe the extracts from just one strain will often satisfy your needs.

Take the oil that you poured into the stainless steel measuring cup and put it on a gentle heating device such as a coffee warmer to evaporate off whatever water remains in the oil. Quite often, it only takes a short time to evaporate the remaining water off, but also some strains produce more natural terpenes than others. These terpenes can cause the oil you now have on the coffee warmer to bubble for quite some time and it may take a while for such oils to cease this activity. When the oil on the coffee warmer has stopped bubbling and there is little or no activity visible, take the oil off the coffee warmer and allow it to cool a bit.

Another way to finish the oil without the use of a coffee warmer is to put the oil in an oven set at 120°C for 30 to 60 minutes. Both of these methods will decarboxylate the finished oil and solvent residue should not be an issue.

Then, using plastic applicators or syringes with no needles that are available in your local drug store, use the plunger to slowly draw the warm oil up into the syringes and allow it to cool. In a short time, the resin will become a thick grease-like substance. Sometimes the resin is so thick that it can be hard to force it out of the syringes when cooled. If such a thing happens, simply put the syringe in a cup of hot water and soon you will be able to squeeze your dosage out more easily. Sometimes a patient will force out too much oil, but if this happens, just pull back on the plunger of the syringe and the excess oil can usually be drawn back into the syringe without too much difficulty.

On average, a dry pound of material will require about 2 gallons (8-9 liters) of solvent to do the two washes that are required. If you plan to produce the oil from more or less starting material, simply do the math to determine roughly how much solvent you will require. From start to finish, it usually takes three to four hours to accomplish the whole process, and then the medicine is sitting there ready to be used.

It should also be mentioned that this oil has an extremely long shelf life. If kept in a cool dark place when stored, it can maintain its medicinal potency for years.

At first, it may seem daunting for some to try to produce their own medicine but in reality this process is extremely simple. All you have to do is carefully follow the instructions and after you produce this medication a couple of times, you will find that it is not much harder to make than a cup of coffee. Once you have produced your own medication, it takes all the mystery out of medicine and you no longer have to rely on doctors in most cases, for now you have become your own doctor.

Have you found any other ways of making the oil?

There are many ways to produce these extracts and I do not claim that my methods are necessarily the best. Indeed the method that we have shown the world would be considered rather crude at best, but still a very pure form of this medication can be produced in this manner. My intention was to present a method of producing the oil with equipment that is readily available so if need be almost everyone could produce their own medicine in a simple manner.

Up until I was raided in 2005, I had used distilling processes to produce the medicine and reclaim the solvents. This method is much less dangerous and is more 'earth friendly', since the solvent is not wasted. But in 2005 the police confiscated my equipment, which forced me to start using rice cookers to accomplish the task.

What other forms of extraction can be used then?

Again, there are a number of extraction methods and I do not profess to be an expert in such things. The problem with scientific methods like noble gas extractions etc. is that most people lack the equipment and knowledge to perform such extractions. That is why we showed the public the simplest possible way to produce this medication themselves.

There are also cold-water extraction methods that can be used to produce the oil. I have only tried to do this type of extraction a couple of times and the results were not as good as expected. Still, I know of people who say that they have produced high quality oil in this manner. Obviously, cold water cannot catch fire or explode, so cold-water extraction methods might certainly be an option, but one must make sure that the oil is decarboxylated properly before it is given to the patient.

What is decarboxylation?

Decarboxylation occurs when the molecules within the oil have been rotated to the delta 9 position with the use of heat so they become more medicinally active. The temperature at which this occurs is debatable, since many reports I have viewed on the subject do not agree. By doing what I have suggested, the oil is heated to temperatures well above that at which decarboxylation is said to occur. The carboxyl group is removed, which then allows the molecules to fit into the CB1 and CB2 receptors of our endocannabinoid system.

Is there a way to make the oil more potent?

There are several ways of increasing the oil's potency, but again many of these methods require specialized equipment and knowledge that the average person does not have. In the past, I have produced such oils and I do consider them more powerful and medicinal but with the laws that are in place and the equipment that is needed, it was impossible for me to produce any amount.

Is there anything I can do when the oil I produced or purchased is not potent enough?

If good starting material is used to produce the oil, this problem should not be encountered, but I'm sure there will be those who will. When treating a serious illness, only the best will do, so if the oil you have does not measure up to the task at hand, I would get some more bud material and produce it properly. With someone's life is hanging in the balance, this is no time to be playing with low quality oil. If you were the one suffering, wouldn't you want the best medication possible? So please try to provide the same for others.

STORAGE

How long can the oil be stored?

From my experience, there is no 'best before date' regarding the storage of hemp medicine. There are three things that can affect the potency of hemp oil: air, light, and heat. I tell people to store this medication in a cool, dark place, but it does not require refrigeration. This takes care of any problems associated with light and heat. As for air causing difficulties, the oil is a thick grease, so air cannot enter it, therefore the oil can be stored for decades and still maintain its potency.

For practical reasons, I usually supply the oil in syringes to make it easier for patients to measure their doses and to prevent contamination. To store oil for a long period of time, I would suggest a stainless steel container or a dark colored bottle with a tight lid. If the oil is stored properly, concern about its date of manufacture can be overlooked for a very long time.

SOLVENTS AND SOLVENT RESIDUE IN THE OIL

Over the years, I have been contacted by a good number of people who were concerned about the possibility that solvent residue could be left behind in the finished oil. From my experience, I feel there is no danger in consuming oil if the instructions we have made available to produce the oil properly are followed. I have been ingesting this oil myself for about ten years with no ill effects. In addition, I have made this oil available to thousands of people and I have received very few complaints. If someone has a problem with the way the oil tastes, it is not caused from solvent residue, instead the cause is usually the natural terpenes, which the oil contains. Some oils have very little taste while others can have an unpleasant flavor, but as far as I know medicine is not supposed to taste good anyway, so I have little concern for such things.

In lab tests performed on the oils I produced, no solvent residue was reported. It seems absurd to me that anyone would worry about solvent residue in the oil when you consider what the medical system has been feeding the public. Liver toxic chemicals, poisons, chemo, radiation, vaccines, etc. It seems to me that anyone worried about being poisoned should be much more concerned with what the medical system supplies, rather than residue from a solvent which has been completely boiled off.

If someone has problems taking the oil, it is usually because an energizing sativa was used to produce the substance. In addition, other problems can arise if the patient is trying to take pharmaceuticals along with the oil treatment, or if he or she is not using it in the right way. In an ideal situation, other family members could take the oil along with the patient. This would help them understand the oil's effects and they would then not worry so much about the effect it is having on the patient. Since they don't know what to expect with the use of the oil, family members often tend to overreact if the patient ingests too much. But the effects will wear off in a short time and the patient will be left unharmed. Therefore, I think other family members should also try the oil in small doses, so they will have a better understanding of this medication.

High-grade hemp oil has the ability to replace the use of most pharmaceuticals but when a patient tries to take pharmaceuticals along with the oil, sometimes problems can arise due to the interactions. Many of the substances doctors provide are poisonous in nature and the oil does not like the presence of such toxins in the patient's body. Usually, shortly after the patient ceases the use of pharmaceutical drugs, any problems they were experiencing simply disappear.

Would it be better or safer to produce the oil using food-grade alcohol?

Often, people tell me that they would prefer to produce the oil using grain alcohol. For some reason, they seem to think that grain alcohol would be safer to use, but in reality it is still poison just like any other solvent. One of the main problems with grain alcohol is that it is almost impossible to find alcohol such as this that is 99 or 100% pure. In most cases, it is hard to find alcohol that is over 95 % and usually the other 5 % will be water. Since this water is present, it makes the alcohol less effective as a solvent and at the end of the process, there will be quite a bit of water left in the oil which must be evaporated off.

From my experience, I do not consider the use of grain alcohol to be any safer than isopropyl alcohol or naphtha to produce the oil. No matter how you look at it, alcohol is poison and when you consume alcohol, it produces a poison high that affects your motor skills and this condition is known as being drunk. I am not saying high-grade oil cannot be produced using grain alcohol. Rather, I am saying you should be aware that this substance is no better or safer than other solvents I have used and in some ways does not work quite as well.

Often, I am contacted by people who wish to extract the oil using such things as butter or olive oil etc. Quite frequently, they ask if I think an extraction done in this manner would produce a medicine with similar potency to the medicine I produce using my method. The answer is no. I consider extractions done in this way to be simply forms of weakened hemp medicine. By volume, there is no possible way that a medication produced like this could have the same potency as the medication I produced. If you had a serious cancer, would you want to treat it with some form of watered-down hemp medicine, or would you prefer to use the real thing in your treatment?

Can hemp oil be used along with alcohol?

I have seen many people who were getting very loud on alcohol calm right down after smoking a joint. There is little doubt alcohol is one of the most destructive things on this planet, but people will be people and many do like their liquor. From our experience, it seems that hemp oil presents no danger to a drinker and can indeed often decrease their intake of this harmful substance. Often heavy drinkers who have taken the hemp oil treatment for their medical problems report that their thirst for alcohol has been greatly diminished, and some have even quit drinking entirely.

What all can hemp oil replace and why did hemp medicine disappear from mainstream medicine?

In most instances, it seems that the oil can replace practically all chemical medications that the medical system provides. Chemicals and poison are not good for us and in my opinion the faster a person can get off these allopathic drugs, the better.

In the 1800s, many pharmaceutical companies that are still in business today in America and elsewhere were producing hemp-based medicines. In fact, if you check the pharmacopoeia from that era, you will find that hemp was an ingredient in many medications these companies produced and was used to treat hundreds of medical problems.

Empiric medicine, medicine produced from plants, did not go out of use because it was not effective. Instead, it was prohibited because it presented a danger to drug companies and other big money interests. There is no question that a great deal of medicine was produced from the hemp plant right up into the early 1900's. Many drug companies produced weak forms of hemp-based medicines for decades, but were afraid of this natural cure-all because they could not patent it. Of course, with farmers freely growing hemp everywhere in North America at the time, anyone could have stumbled onto the truth as I did.

I think the drug companies of that era lived in fear that this would happen and if the public learned the truth, it could drive them out of business. Drug companies and other big money interests definitely wanted hemp prohibited, since this plant presented a real danger to their profit margins. I guess this just goes to show you that drug companies were no better than they are today. To them, it's all about profit, and concern for the patient's well-being means nothing.

CHAPTER 3

WHAT THE OIL DOES AND HOW IT WORKS

From my experience, all forms of disease and conditions are treatable and often curable with the use of high-grade hemp oil as a treatment. Due to its harmless nature as a medicine, hemp oil is in a class all by itself. Even something like aspirin tablets that is looked upon as being harmless by the public causes thousands of deaths worldwide each year. If you are looking for a safe medication, look no further than what the hemp plant can provide. On top of all that, it's a medicine we can all grow and produce ourselves. In addition, in the majority of cases there is no need for a doctor's supervision with its use.

When the hemp plant is grown for medicinal use, you now have your own means of producing an effective medicine that is much safer and more medicinally active than anything our current medical system provides. For instance, you still may require a doctor to set your broken leg, but you will no longer need the chemical medications they have been providing us with in the past. Hemp is medicine for the masses, which works well on every condition I have treated, and no one has the right to control its use.

We all have different body chemistry and we all have different tolerances for practically everything. So it is up to each and every one of us to determine for ourselves how much oil we require to maintain good health. Many patients have come to me after years of treatment by the medical system and they did not even have a diagnosis for their conditions. Still, the oil was able to exercise its amazing healing power and their medical problems were solved.

Another aspect of the use of hemp as medicine is its anti-aging properties. As we age, our vital organs deteriorate and of course, this impairs the function of these organs. Over time, hemp oil rejuvenates vital organs even if taken in small doses, but obviously it would work much faster if more were taken quickly. It is very common for patients to report to me that they feel 20 to 30 years younger after only ingesting the oil for a short time.

Now let's take it to the next level. What about people who ingest larger quantities of oil over a longer period of time, like I have? After ten years of rather erratic treatment, my body does not appear to be that of a 62-year-old man. Instead, it has the appearance of someone who is a great deal younger and I no longer carry any excess fat around. I can honestly say that since I began taking the oil, it appears that the aging process has reversed itself and I have grown younger instead of growing older.

When I have the oil at my disposal, I like to take about a quarter of a gram a day. Of course, due to short supply, quite often I must go without, so my own treatment has been erratic to say the least. From my own experience with the oil, I cannot help but wonder what would happen if a person were to ingest even larger quantities over a longer period of time. If a person were to do this, could one actually reverse the aging process or at the very least slow it down? By all appearances, this did seem to be the results, which I achieved and I have seen the oil do the same for many others.

Someday soon, when I have enough oil, I intend to start taking a gram a day for a year to see what effect it has on my body. Many people who have taken the oil have stated that they thought it to be the fountain of youth. From my own experiences with the oil, I believe this statement to be well founded.

Throughout our lives, the system has told us they want preventative medicine. Now what greater preventative medicine could there possibly be than hemp oil? Judging from what I have seen, if children were given tiny doses of oil each day much the same as a supplement, diseases like cancer, diabetes, MS, and many other conditions could become quite rare. I am not talking about getting the kiddies high, for once a person gets accustomed to this medication, they do not even feel or exhibit effects from the oil they are ingesting. Hemp oil is a safe and harmless medication that all age groups can benefit from and that goes for our children, too.

A study that was done in the 1980's by Melanie Dreher proved that the healthiest babies on earth were born to mothers in Jamaica who used a great deal of hemp. If ingesting or smoking hemp does not harm a baby in its developmental stages in the womb, why would it not be safe for children of all ages to use? Therefore if the system truly wants preventative medicine, here it is. Now why are they refusing to use it?

I know the word cure-all is a hard pill to swallow. When I worked in the medical system, such terms were thought of as a joke but when you see for yourself what this oil can do like I did, what else could it be called? What other medicine works on everything and in many cases can cure thought-to-be incurable conditions? What else can heal diabetic ulcers, skin cancers, or third degree burns in no time, leaving no scars?

Many others and I have gone through mountains of so-called scientific studies, but I found them very misleading and most were little more than doubletalk. The vast majority of these studies were about synthetic THC, which bears little resemblance to natural THC and its associated cannabinoids found in the hemp plant. After studying all this scientific jargon, I had learned what amounted to nothing but the oil continued to work the miracles, so who was I to question it?

I had just about given up hope that we would ever find out why the oil worked so well for all these different medical conditions. Then, a short time ago, a lady named Batya Stark provided me with what I think is some of the missing pieces to the puzzle. She sent me a great deal of information about melatonin and the pineal gland, which produces it. It seems that the pineal gland is in the driver's seat along with our endocannabinoid system when it comes to healing and regulating our bodies, in many ways.

The melatonin this gland produces is an essential part of healing and it is the greatest anti-oxidant known to man. When the function of the pineal gland becomes impaired from chemicals or aging, it produces much less melatonin and therefore our bodies become more susceptible to disease. Studies have been released that show people suffering from cancer and other serious conditions have low levels of melatonin in their bodies. Also, studies have shown that just smoking hemp can raise the melatonin levels in our bodies, so one can just imagine what the concentrated oil can do to increase melatonin levels.

As we age, we acidify and cancer thrives in an acidic environment. So bringing the body's pH level up is very important when you are suffering from cancer and many other conditions. While the oil is working its magic, simple things like watermelon and lemon juice can be ingested to raise the body's pH very rapidly. As the patient's pH goes up, cancer cells will find it harder and harder to survive, so you can see why I consider the patient's pH to be so important.

Tumors are simply the symptom of an underlying condition that is present in the bodies of people who are suffering from cancer. To treat the patient successfully, this underlying condition must be treated to cure the cancer and prevent it from returning.

Melatonin is the greatest antioxidant on earth and travels to every cell in our bodies. It is one of the keys to good health. I am not just talking about treating cancer, it seems that melatonin levels are important in the treatment of many serious conditions. Now all you have to do is connect the dots, it all adds up. Hemp oil promotes full body healing and raises melatonin levels thousands of times higher than normal. When the pineal gland produces vast amounts of melatonin, it causes no harm to the body, but it can have a dramatic effect on the condition you are suffering from.

For the most part, we think the effects of the oil can be greatly improved if the patient's pH is raised while the oil is detoxifying their system. I have seen patients that did nothing other than ingest the oil and it still worked miracles, but I believe anything natural that can make the treatment even more effective should be given strong consideration.

I and those around me are not doctors or scientists and we can only wonder why it was not them who brought this to the public's attention instead of us. After years of research on our part, the endocannabinoid system and a healthy pineal gland are the only things we have found that connects all the dots and explains in a simple way why this medicine can do what it does.

Now we must look at what could be causing the function of our pineal gland to become impaired. Much of the time, it can be caused by our own lifestyles and things like cell phones that we come in contact with every day. Companies that produce cell phones do not like to talk about it and would prefer that we did the same but our bodies run on electrical impulses. Now do you think it's a good idea to put something against your head that produces microwave radiation which can interfere with the electrical impulses in our bodies that keep us healthy?

Cell phones are just one of the culprits. Look at studies of cancer rates in people who live near and around high-tension power lines. I did not understand the importance of all this until a friend of mine cured his heart condition by having two electrical problems in his home repaired. It's frightening that so many things we come into contact with frequently can harm our health but still there are a number of other things that do the same.

Can someone out there give me a rational explanation as to why fluoride seems to be in everything these days? Please do not try to tell me it's to prevent tooth decay, because even a formally uneducated country boy like me knows better than that. Did Hitler not use fluoride in his death camps to keep the inmates calm so they would not try to escape or revolt, and do you think that they might just be doing the same to us? I have been told that even the antidepressant Prozac can contain a great deal of fluoride and I expect that many other medications are little different.

Since the only use for fluoride that I know of is to keep the masses from revolting, I strongly suspect this is the reason why we are being exposed to so much of the substance. It may be just my suspicious nature at play, but does what's going on currently not smell a little like a death camp to you? I can only wonder what effect all this fluoride we are ingesting is having on our brains and our pineal glands but I fully expect that it is doing a great deal of damage.

What about the effects of all those chemicals and poisons the doctors have been feeding to us? Would these substances interfere with the function of our pineal glands and could they also acidify our bodies more quickly? I will leave that one for the medical experts to figure out.

What about our food supply? The meat that is sold to the public in Canada and some other countries cannot even be sold in Europe. It seems that Canadian and American beef is looked down upon by Europeans because it has too many contaminants like antibiotics and growth hormones. Do you not find it strange that the meat we eat is deemed unhealthy in Europe, yet it is freely sold to anyone that is misinformed enough to eat it back in North America?

Now what about fruits, vegetables, and all the other fare we find in supermarkets in North America? We all know that most of these commodities contain pesticides, additives, preservatives, and many have even been genetically modified etc. How could anyone consider such things in their diet to be safe and why do we allow companies like Monsanto to genetically modify our food when madness like this should not even be allowed?

Over time, these harmful substances accumulate in our bodies and when we become sick, many wonder why because they think that they have been eating properly. With no one in authority to protect the consumer, just going to the supermarket can be a life-threatening experience. As you can plainly see, many governments are in fact doing nothing to protect their citizens from big corporations that care little about the harm caused to those who consume their goods.

Governments are supposed to be working for the greater good of their people but obviously this is not what has been taking place. I think it's just about time that we all stand as one and tell those who are currently representing us that we have had enough of their corruption and manipulation. If those who are now in authority will not comply, then we should simply replace them with someone who will. It's plain to see that we cannot go on like this. Without honest representation we are lost, so let's get to work and do what needs to be done.

PROTOCOL AND DOSAGE INFORMATION

Is there a protocol for the treatment?
There is a protocol and it should be followed to ensure that the treatment is effective. Small amounts of oil can be used to treat skin cancer and other conditions topically or it can be vaporized and inhaled to help treat lung conditions. The oil may also be absorbed into the body if used in the form of a suppository or, of course, it can be ingested directly by mouth. To treat internal cancers, the patient should ingest the oil as quickly as possible. In general, you always want to get this medication to the area that is causing the problem in the most sensible way. For example, if you were treating bowel cancer, the most effective means of treatment would likely be to take the oil in suppository form.

The average patient can ingest a full 60-gram cancer treatment in about 90 days. People who have endured radiation and chemotherapy damage, or patients who have suffered for years with MS and other serious conditions will find in some cases that their medical problems can take quite some time to heal.

Those who have suffered serious damage from the medical system and are just starting treatment must realize that this natural oil does not produce an instant cure. Often, these patients require much more oil and it will need to be taken over a longer period. Such patients should try to ingest 120 to 180 grams over six months to undo the harm all the chemo and radiation has left behind and to repair damage caused by other long-term illnesses and what was used to treat them. Once the patient is cured and all the damage has been undone or the condition has been brought under control, I recommend they then continue to take a maintenance dose of 1 to 2 grams of oil per month to maintain good health. For an adult, this would equal about a drop a day, and once they are accustomed to its use, they do not even feel its effects, so I really cannot imagine that this is too high a price to pay for good health.

I suggest that patients start with three doses per day about the size of a half a grain of dry short-grained rice. A dose such as this would equal about ¼ of a drop, so as you can see, in most cases beginners should start with very tiny doses.

The only time I would recommend that patients start out with larger doses would be to get them off addictive and dangerous pain medications quickly or if they were right at death's door. When people who are using such medications begin the oil treatment, they usually cut their pain medications in half. The object is to ingest enough oil to take care of the pain and to help the patient free themselves from the use of these dangerous addictive pharmaceutical drugs. Taking the oil makes it much easier for the patient to accomplish this task and they will suffer less withdrawal problems because the oil works wonderfully to help break addictions.

For those who are in this situation, I think their first dose should be about double what the average beginner would ingest. Then they should up their dosage as quickly as possible until they reach the point where they require no other medications to control pain. When taking people off medications such as morphine, you may encounter some problems. Sometimes when you mix oil and morphine, it can make the effects of the morphine even more pronounced and the patient may begin to hallucinate.

This is only a short-term drawback, since as the patient's intake of morphine is reduced, the hallucinations will diminish until they no longer take place. In most cases, getting patients off these harmful substances presents few problems, and this can usually be accomplished in a very short time. As they continue to increase their dosage, the patient will develop a higher tolerance and soon they will no longer even feel the oil's effects. Once this occurs, they can then ingest whatever amount of oil that is needed very quickly until they are healed.

After four days of taking a beginner's dosage, most people are able to increase the amount they are ingesting. I suggest that this should take place about every four days, because this allows the patient time to build up their tolerance for this substance. It takes the average person four to five weeks to get to the point where they can ingest a gram per day. This means the patient would be ingesting 8 to 9 drops of high quality oil every eight hours. Once they reach this dosage, the patient can then continue at this rate until the condition disappears or is under control.

Many patients develop a tolerance for this medication very quickly and can take the oil at a much faster rate than others. If you happen to be one of these people, please feel free to ingest this substance as quickly as you like, since the end result will be you will heal that much faster. I always caution patients to stay in their own comfort zone with the use of this medication, but if the oil can be taken more quickly, it can give many patients a better chance to survive.

This method allows the body to build up its tolerance slowly and after four to five weeks, most people have no problem ingesting a gram a day or even more in some cases. For the average person who increases their dosage every four days, usually few problems are encountered. In fact, I have received reports from some individuals who took the oil, which stated that they felt as though they never even got high during treatment. We all have different tolerances for any medication, so I feel that it's best to allow the patient to determine what amount of this substance they are comfortable in taking.

Your size and body weight have little to do with your tolerance for hemp oil. I have seen beginners who were very large men take one drop of this oil and within an hour, they could not even get off the chesterfield. While their wives who were much smaller could take the same dose and feel nothing at all. So, as you can see, size is not an important factor when it comes to determining how much the patient can take, it's really more about the tolerance of the patient themselves.

Be aware when commencing treatment with this medication that it will lower your blood pressure. If you are currently taking blood pressure medication, check your pressure often, for it's very likely that you will no longer require anything other than the oil to control your blood pressure in a very short time. In addition, if the patient is a diabetic, they should monitor their blood sugar. In most cases, their need for insulin will diminish and some will no longer require the use of this substance at all.

When people are taking the oil, I like to see them stay within their comfort zone, but the truth is the faster they can take it, the better the chance of surviving.

I had one man with an extremely low tolerance take seven months to ingest the 60g treatment. It did cure his terminal lymphoma, but I would have much preferred it if he could have taken the entire treatment more quickly.

Luckily, I seldom run into patients who take so long to ingest the treatment but it does happen. I have even seen patients who have taken the whole treatment in a month and were able to cure their terminal cancers. Therefore, the rate the oil can be ingested for the most part depends on the patients themselves and on how quickly they can build their tolerance.

At the end of their treatment, most people continue taking these extracts, but at a much reduced rate. As I mentioned before, about one to two grams a month, which equals about a drop of oil before bedtime each night, would be a good maintenance dose.

I do not like to see people overdosing on the oil, but an overdose does no harm, so don't panic if this should occur. The main side effect of this medication is sleep and rest, which plays an important role in the healing process. Usually, within an hour after taking a dose, the oil's effects are telling the patient to lay down and relax. Don't fight the sleepy feeling, just make yourself comfortable and allow the oil to give you the rest you require. In most cases, within a month, the daytime tiredness associated with this treatment fades away but the patient continues to sleep very well at night.

I tell patients who are dying from cancer that the oil will do one of two things: it will either cure their cancer and they will continue to live on, or, in cases where it is too late to affect a cure, the oil will ease their way out and they can at least die without much suffering and maintain their dignity.

Hemp oil has a very high success rate in the treatment of cancer and most tend to survive. Unfortunately, many people who come to me have been badly damaged by the medical system with their chemo and radiation, etc. The damage such treatments cause have a lasting effect and people who have suffered these so-called treatments are the hardest to cure. But don't despair, for even if you have been badly damaged, this oil still has a 70 to 80% success rate.

If produced and used properly, hemp medicine is the greatest natural healer on this planet bar none. No matter what a person is suffering from, they should give the oil a try and see what it can do to help them. If you are truly tired of suffering, give yourself a break and try something that really does work for a change. Once you experience what this medication can do, you will understand why history and I both call hemp medicine a cure-all.

OTHER NATURAL THINGS YOU CAN DO WHICH COULD HELP

When patients come to me for oil to treat their cancer, the first thing I tell them to do is change their diets. Try to stay away from animal protein as much as possible, since this type of protein promotes cancer growth. Get a juicing machine and start eating as many raw fruits and vegetables as possible, because plant protein fights the growth of cancer. Stop using sugar and replace its use with natural sweeteners like raw honey.

Get the patient's pH up as quickly as possible by having then ingest such things as watermelon and lemon juice etc. Cancer likes an acidic environment and when you raise the body's pH, it makes it very hard for cancer cells to survive.

Decades ago, researchers had great results treating cancer with mega doses of vitamin C, which was injected right into the patient's blood stream in much the same way doctors inject chemo, but without the devastating side effects which can cause the patient's death. Therefore, I think large doses of vitamins could be of great benefit to patients suffering from serious conditions like cancer.

Also have the patient start eating the seeds from two to three apples every day, this will give them a good daily dose of B17, which is also known as laetrile. Years ago, there was a lot of propaganda about this treatment not being safe, but these allegations proved to be false. In reality, B17 in its own right has a pretty good track record in the treatment of cancer. There are also other natural things such as wheat grass and blue green algae that you may find of benefit as well. A few years ago, a doctor in Italy was even curing some types of cancer with the use of baking soda, so we must keep our minds open to all possibilities.

Many people who have used the oil to treat their cancers did not change a thing but the oil still worked its magic and they were healed. Still, if you have a serious condition like cancer, I think it's a good idea to take other natural things which may help the oil eradicate the cancer more quickly and give you a better chance to survive.

The most important thing of all is that people have to realize that for the most part what the medical system provides does much more harm than good. That is the reason I tell people who contact me that if they want to survive, it's best to stay as far away from the medical system as possible.

This is the sad state the medical system we have today is really in and it will not change until people who work within this system finally realize that chemicals and poison do not heal. As far as I am concerned, what most doctors practice today could hardly be considered medicine. In my opinion it would be much more accurate to call it by its real name, madness.

From my point of view, anyone with cancer should be doing everything they possibly can to optimize their chance of survival. So, by all means, take hemp oil to treat your cancer but I think it would be best to include other natural beneficial treatments as well.

ROUTES OF ADMINISTRATION

What routes of administration of the oil do you recommend and what are their respective advantages?

I always suggest to patients that they should ingest the oil by mouth or in suppository for to treat internal conditions, or to just bring their bodies back to a state of good health. After a few decades of being exposed to toxins in our day-to-day lives, even those who think of themselves as being healthy should consider ingesting a full 60g treatment to detoxify their bodies before these toxins can cause problems with their health.

To treat many illnesses such as hemorrhoids or prostate cancer etc., it may be best to use the oil in the form of a suppository. Most people don't realize it, but taking the oil into your body in this manner is one of the most effective ways to accomplish the task.

I think it's of benefit to the patient for the oil to be administered as close as possible to a tumor or whatever is being treated. Therefore if you have bowel problems, suppositories would likely work best, but if you have something like throat or stomach cancer, etc. I would ingest the oil by mouth.

For years, doctors and researchers have been injecting tumors in lab animals with THC and they have achieved good results. Yet, sadly, they will not do the same to a dying cancer patient, so once more this highlights the failure of our medical system to do what's right for the patient. If doctors would only recognize this amazing medication for what it is and begin to work properly with this substance, many who are now dying could be saved.

Often, patients come to me with lung cancer and other lung conditions. For such people, I recommend the use of a vaporizer in addition to ingesting the oil. Vaporizing this medication along with ingesting these extracts can have a very beneficial effect for those suffering from lung cancers or other lung conditions. All a patient has to do is ingest their regular dose and then warm up a vaporizer and inhale the vaporized cannabinoids into their lungs. This could be done every eight hours when they are ingesting their regular dosage and it would only require the patient to inhale the vaporized cannabinoids a couple of times at each setting. By using this method, the lung cancer is being attacked from both directions and this can greatly increase the effectiveness of the treatment.

In most cases, the tumors just disappear, but I have heard that some patients have actually coughed up dead pieces of the tumors which have been present in their lungs. I am sure this is not an experience one would enjoy, but it is the natural way our lungs rid themselves of things that should not be there.

In addition, I know patients who have passed tumors during bowel movements, but of course, this too is only natural. In some instances, these dead encapsulated tumors may have to be removed surgically, if they are too big to pass by natural means, so in a situation like this, a doctor would be required.

Judging from those I have provided the oil to who were suffering from various forms of cancer, I do not know of any type of cancer that this oil would not be effective to treat. To me, all forms of cancer are curable no matter where it chooses to manifest itself in your body. The less damage the patient has received from the medical system, the better their chance of recovery, so in my opinion those who wish to cure their cancer should use this proven natural method.

For topical use, the oil can be mixed with skin creams, suntan lotions etc. However, for serious skin conditions, I advise that just the oil in its purest form should be used. Mixing these extracts with anything will reduce the potency of this medication. But still, many of these weakened forms of hemp medicine can be quite effective in treating skin problems and things of that nature.

Often for people with very bad skin conditions which are spread over large areas of their body, I recommend the use of a cannabis tincture. A tincture is simply oil mixed with alcohol or some such carrier. When one uses an eyedropper to apply a tincture to a skin condition, the alcohol causes one drop to spread out over quite a large area. The alcohol then evaporates off in just a few seconds, leaving the area covered with a thin film of oil.

Tinctures are a cost effective way to administer these extracts over large areas and the patients themselves can adjust the strength of such a tincture to suit their needs. If one desires the tincture to be stronger, simply add more oil; if they want to weaken it, then just add more alcohol.

Do you think hemp tinctures could possibly be as potent as your hemp oil?

By volume, it would be impossible for a hemp tincture to be as potent as pure oil. A patient could ingest their doses mixed with alcohol, but what good would taking this medication with alcohol do the patient? The oil is the medicine and mixing it with alcohol or other such carriers in my opinion is not of any benefit for internal use.

Currently, there is a drug company selling an overpriced cannabis based tincture called *Sativex*, which is sprayed under the tongue for pain relief etc. I have provided extracts to patients who were using this substance and after experiencing the effects of the oil, they had no further need to purchase *Sativex*, since they found the oil I provided to be more effective. For topical conditions, a tincture can be used to make the oil go further but for a serious skin condition or infection, I would prefer to see that pure oil is used in its treatment.

What are the main uses for topical application and have you witnessed any allergic reactions to the oil?

I have found tinctures to be effective in treating many skin conditions and using the oil in this manner can be much less wasteful. For people who are concerned about their complexions, simply mixing a small amount of these extracts with their favorite face cream and giving themselves a good facial can have dramatic results.

Herpes, skin cancer, warts, moles, and other skin conditions can be treated with pure oil with no allergic reactions that I know of. In reality, the only adverse reaction I have witnessed when the oil is used topically was caused by the bandages used to cover it. When you use a bandage for extended periods, it can cause the area covered with the sticky portion of the bandage to become irritated. In such a situation one simply has to stop using the bandages for a day or two and the condition will disappear. I also feel that the use of waterproof bandages should be avoided, since they cut off the air circulation to the area being treated. Therefore, I do not consider their use to be of benefit.

Another thing I must mention is that these extracts do not allow the bandages to stick to the wound or infection which is being healed. This may not sound too important, but if you have ever gone through the agony of removing a bandage which has stuck to a wound, you will understand what I mean.

When I was in Canada, I often blended oils from different indica varieties, because they can vary so much in their medical virtues. By doing this, I found these blended extracts had a better overall healing effect on many conditions, so if you are planning to produce oil on a larger scale, you might consider doing the same.

Can you combine various types of administration of the oil?

All different ways of administering the oil can be combined with no harmful side effects and indeed doing so can be of great benefit in some situations. For instance, if I had lung cancer, I could combine ingesting the extract with the use of suppositories and I would also vaporize the oil so the cannabinoids could be inhaled directly into my lungs. Both oral ingestion and suppositories seem to work well in the treatment of lung cancer and vaporizing the oil can also be of benefit for those who suffer from this condition.

Scientific literature says the body cannot process THC unless it is dissolved in animal fat. Would it not be more efficient to use the oil that way?

I really have little concern about what scientific literature says and I do not think that animal fat is good for patients who are suffering from conditions like cancer. From my experience, the oil does not have to be mixed with anything else to be effective. Since I have taken it many times without food and still felt its effects, I think there is a good chance that what we have been told is wrong. If the body cannot process THC without being mixed with animal fat, why could I still feel the effects of the oil? In addition when cannabis is smoked, there is no animal fat present in the joint, so how do people get high?

By using processes which dissolve the THC and other cannabinoids into animal fat, butter or lard etc., I feel the potency of the medicine is reduced. It is the oil that is doing the healing, not butter or animal fat, therefore I think this medication should be used in its purest form to achieve maximum effectiveness. If I took a person who had two skin cancers and I treated one with pure oil and the other with an oil animal fat mix, I have little doubt the cancer treated with the pure oil would heal much faster and more effectively.

SMOKING CANNABIS

Can you compare the medical value of smoking and eating hemp?

When a person smokes a joint, over 90% of the medicinal aspects of the plant material just went up in smoke. It's ironic for me to see patients who have taken chemotherapy smoking cannabis to reduce their nausea, for they are smoking the very substance which, if taken properly, could very well cure them.

To me, there is little or no comparison between smoking cannabis and ingesting the essential oil from this plant to treat a serious medical condition. If you are simply seeking a little relief from your condition, smoking cannabis may be of some benefit. But if you want to treat the condition properly, ingesting the oil is the best way to accomplish this. There is no question that even smoking cannabis does have some medicinal benefits, but don't expect to cure a serious condition in this manner.

What is smoked marijuana good for from a medical point of view?

From a medical point of view, smoking cannabis hemp has limited medical value when compared to ingesting these extracts. Smoking pot can often have an effect on blood sugar levels for those with diabetes and it can also

51

help reduce ocular pressure for people who suffer with glaucoma. We all know of hemp's ability to reduce nausea and smoking this substance will often help combat the pain associated with many medical conditions.

Simply smoking a good indica strain does tend to make a person relax, which in itself can be quite beneficial. Smoking pot can help reduce the symptoms of many conditions such as MS and is often very beneficial to those with spasmodic conditions. There is no shortage of evidence which clearly shows that even smoking cannabis can do much to help the well-being of countless people worldwide. But, from my point of view, why just reduce the symptoms when a cure or much better control for the problem may be possible if the medicine is taken properly in the form of an extract.

There is little comparison between smoking hemp and ingesting hemp oil. Smoking is the least effective method of using hemp as a medicine. The healing power of hemp is magnified many times when the concentrated essential oil of the hemp plant is produced. If you want to see the real medicinal magic in this plant, start ingesting high-grade hemp oil. When one starts ingesting the raw, unburned THC and its associated cannabinoids, medical miracles are often the result.

HEMP OIL VERSUS HASHISH

What is the main difference between hemp oil and hash?
Hemp oil is simply the essential oil of the cannabis hemp plant and it is manufactured from the resins this plant produces. Hashish is also produced from the same resins and it is compressed into pieces of hash in a variety of different ways. But even the highest grades of hash usually contain plant matter, dust, and other contaminants. Since hash is not nearly as pure as the essential oil, it is only logical that it would not be as effective as a medicine due to the impurities it contains. In addition, resins used to produce hashish are not decarboxylated and this too would reduce the medicinal value of hash when compared to oils that have been produced properly.

Many people tend to call the oil I produce, hash oil and a variety of other names as well, like honey oil and weed oil etc., yet in reality there is no such thing as hash oil. Why would anyone go through all the effort to produce a large piece of hash, then dissolve it in solvent so the impurities can be filtered out to produce the oil?

Honey oil is another term we often hear, but it simply is in reference to the amber color some extracts exhibit, which gives them the appearance of honey. Other terms like weed oil are usually used to describe low-grade extracts, which have been produced from leaves and cuttings, but I believe that these less potent extracts should only be used to treat skin conditions.

Would eating hashish have the same effects as eating the oil you produce?

I do not believe that eating hashish to treat a medical condition would produce the medicinal benefits of which these extracts are capable. Hash usually contains many medicinally undesirable contaminates which have been removed from these extracts if they have been properly produced. When making the oil, the heating process involved causes the oil to become decarboxylated by the time the oil is ready to use. This decarboxylation process does not occur when producing hashish because the resins are never heated to this extent, hash is decarboxylated as it burns while smoking and this increases its potency.

At one time, I used to eat small amounts of hash and I could definitely feel its presence but the oils I produced had a much more profound and lasting effect. Therefore, ingesting hash to treat a medical condition would be far less effective than ingesting high-grade extracts. Unless the resin within the hash could be purified by having the contaminates removed and the resin was then decarboxylated.

INTOXICATION

Do people get high when eating the oil?

Of course a patient can get high if they ingest too much of this extract, especially if they are new to its effects. Still, if one uses common sense and starts with small doses and then gradually increase their dosage over time, in many cases, 'getting high' can be completely avoided or its effects can be greatly diminished. Also, suppositories containing small amounts of these extracts can be used with great success to treat many different conditions and although some claim that getting high can be avoided by using suppositories, after using suppositories myself, I would tend to disagree.

I really don't understand why some people are so concerned about getting high on this oil anyway, since it presents no danger to the patient.

The public should be much more concerned about the effects of treatments like chemo and radiation rather than hemp oil. After all, when the medical system gives you enough poison to cause all your hair to fall out, that should tell you something.

Quite some time ago, a young man called me to ask about how to produce the oil for his mother who had cancer. I explained the process to him over the phone and told him how to administer the medication he intended to produce. About four days later, I received a call from his mother and she was very angry. She shouted, "I took a dose of that stuff three days ago and its effects have just finally worn off!"

I calmed her down and asked her how much she had taken and she said she had ingested one gram. I asked her why she had taken so much, as I would never suggest that someone start their treatment in such a manner. She said her son had told her that I said the medicine was safe. I explained to her that this medication is safe but you have to begin with small doses three times a day and then increase your doses about every four days. I explained that apparently her son had produced the medicine properly but he had obviously overlooked the instructions on how to use it.

She then began taking the medicine the way I directed and a few weeks later, I received another call from her. She was very apologetic about her first call to me, but I was well aware of why it had taken place. I told her I understood the effects of an overdose such as the one she had taken and that such a dose would probably have knocked an elephant off its feet. I then explained such things should be avoided, especially for those who are not experienced with the effects these extracts can have. The fact that she had never used hemp in the past and did not understand its effects, combined with the large dose she ingested, had probably given her quite a scare. She informed me that she had done as I suggested and had increased her doses six times. She then stated, "You know, Mr. Simpson, I like taking this stuff, and I can see how much it is helping me already." She then thanked me for explaining to her son how to produce this medication and, to the best of my knowledge, she is still alive and well today.

A year or so before I left Canada, a man from Prince Edward Island who had terminal non-Hodgkin's lymphoma came to me for help. Normally, I tell people to start the oil treatment with very small doses but this man was in very bad shape and did not have long to live. I asked him if he had ever smoked cannabis before, and he replied that he had smoked it many times, so I told him that under the circumstances I would suggest he get this medication into him as soon as possible. He had no fear of smoking hemp and from his own experience, he knew that hemp presented no danger to him. So he took my advice and started ingesting the oil as quickly as possible. Twenty-eight days later, he came to see me and I hardly recognized him, since his appearance had changed so radically and the improvement in his health was more than apparent. I asked him how much oil he had taken. To this he replied, "All ten tubes!"

I was very surprised and I guess it must have showed on my face, so he asked if he had done something wrong. I replied that no, on the contrary, he had done everything right but I had to ask him how he had managed to ingest 60 grams of this extract so quickly. He explained that he began by taking doses every six hours and every time he took a dose, he increased the amount of oil he was ingesting. He stated that for the first week and a half, he was 'high as a kite' and could hardly get to his feet. Then all of a sudden the oil stopped producing this effect, since his body had built up its tolerance for the substance. After this occurred, he stated that he just flew through the rest of the medication. About two weeks after this visit, he called me and told me that he had been in for tests and the results were he was now cancer free. This man had eliminated his terminal cancer in 28 days using cannabis extracts and I am sure that there are many others who would have little difficulty in doing the same.

ADDICTION TO THC

There is no physical addiction to THC or the hemp oil, which contains it. About one in ten people have addictive personalities and will develop a psychological dependency to many things they are using. We see them around us all the time, these are the same people who drink 15 cups of coffee a day and tend to overdo the use of other things as well. When a person with a personality like this smokes cannabis, often they do overuse it but they are not physically addicted.

A true physical addiction can only occur when substances such as opiate-based pharmaceuticals, hard street drugs, and alcohol, etc. are ingested. Such drugs can do harm to the brain and the damage can be observed in brain scans performed on people who overuse these substances. These are the same drugs which are largely responsible for our escalating crime and addiction rates. Those who are addicted to these substances will often beg, borrow, or steal whatever is needed to replenish their supply, but the use of cannabis does not present such problems.

You cannot develop a physical addiction to cannabis since it is non-addictive and this fact has even been acknowledged by some governments. Yet, police forces like the RCMP in Canada still visit schools and tell children that hemp is addictive and causes cancer. Not much wonder our children are beginning to question what they are being told, since in reality the information they are being fed is nothing more than a pack of lies.

Do you think getting high poses any serious dangers when compared with the effects of other medications?

Getting high on cannabis poses practically no danger to the user or society in general. Unfortunately, the same cannot be said for many addictive and dangerous pharmaceutical medications and street drugs like alcohol, which for the most part do nothing but harm. I do not know of anyone who has died due to their use of hemp medicines, but I do know of vast numbers who are in an early grave because they used pharmaceuticals.

Do you get feedback from people after treatment?

In many cases, people came to me for the treatment and I never heard from them again. This I think is due to the illegal nature of this medicine and the fact that most people want to avoid trouble with the legal system. After many patients receive the oil, I hear nothing more from them because they often think the police may have tapped my telephone or some such thing.

Since I do not want patients bothered by the authorities, I do not insist they remain in contact. Often I receive calls from patients looking for the treatment who know others who have used the oil to treat their cancer or other conditions. Usually I would ask the person who calls the name of the people they know who solved their medical issues by using the oil. Quite often, the name they would give me rang a bell and in many cases that is how I found out that the extract had worked for them.

In addition, there are a good number of people who do stay in touch with me after treatment and their input has been priceless. On average, there is about one person in ten who will freely tell the world what had healed them but the majority of patients tend to remain more or less quiet. The false propaganda about this plant which has been drummed into our heads often causes other family members to stand against this medication's use. This situation makes it very hard on the patient and I have even seen some who ceased to use these extracts due to the interference of others. Then, quite often, the patient dies a horrible death and the person who interrupted the treatment which could have saved their life walks away thinking they have done nothing wrong. What a shame so many people simply regurgitate the nonsense they have been fed by others without truly understanding anything about the subject themselves.

Another problem is that many patients often seem to feel ashamed that they had to use an illegal substance in their treatment and they do not want others to know. Those who refuse to speak out about what this natural medication did for them are obviously individuals who care for nothing but themselves. Since most people will not come forward, it makes my task that much harder and many will continue to die because those who have used these extracts refuse to discuss what they have witnessed.

Have you heard any negative criticism of hemp oil?

Over the years, what I am doing has attracted a great deal of criticism from those who wished to bring my activities to a halt. Even individuals like Lester Grinspoon who for some reason is looked upon as being an authority on the subject has made outrageous statements against me and this medication's use.

The same can also be said about Allen St Pierre the national director of NORML in the US. Quite some time ago, Mr. St Pierre e-mailed me and stated that the oil I produce is snake oil and the claims I am making have not been proven.

To me this seems like a rather strange statement to be coming from the national director of an organization that is supposedly trying to legalize cannabis hemp. If they doubted my claims, why did they not investigate and prove it to themselves before making statements which would later come back to haunt them? From my perspective, those who have done such things are either completely oblivious to the truth or they may have even made these comments to receive financial gain. Other than the reasons just stated, I cannot imagine why anyone would try to hold this medicine's use back from the public.

Quite a while ago, I attended a meeting sponsored by NORML which took place at Dalhousie University in Halifax. Mark St Maurice, a spokesman for NORML in Canada, stated that hemp is not a cure-all and they had produced the oil to treat a woman with cancer but it did not work. I asked him what they had done and he replied that they had made a small amount of oil for her and they have heard nothing more. So to clarify matters I stated, "You don't know if it worked or not and since you obviously did not follow any protocol at all, how can you say it did not work?" There were patients in attendance that day who had treated their terminal cancer and other conditions successfully with the oil, so what this man was trying to tell them did not go over well.

As far as I am concerned, NORML is mostly just a pack of lawyers trying to fill their pockets by keeping hemp illegal. Unfortunately for us all, there are vast numbers of individuals who work in many fields that are trying to do the same. The only sensible reason I can see as to why they are doing such things would be to protect their own incomes and positions. Instead of doing what's right for the people, they simply continue on with all the propaganda and misinformation to fulfill their own agendas. Fortunately, those who actually do know something about this subject tend to be in agreement with me, but soon I hope to see all this nonsense come to an end.

SIDE EFFECTS

Is it safe to use hemp oil?
The safety of this medicine is beyond compare and from what I have witnessed, it is no more dangerous than drinking a cup of fresh water. Even if a person overdoses badly, there is no harm done to them once the effects of the oil wears off. The most common side effect we have noted with people ingesting hemp oil for their medical conditions is a great deal of rest and a smile on their faces.

How is the oil usually tolerated?
We all have different tolerances for powerful medications, so I encourage patients to stay in their own comfort zone when determining what dosage they will ingest. Most people's tolerance builds very quickly and, on average, a normal person usually takes about 90 days to ingest the 60-gram treatment. 60 grams of properly produced oil seems to be able to cure most cancers unless the patient was badly damaged by the medical system with their chemo and radiation, etc.

Patients who have suffered the effects of chemo and radiation require more oil to undo the damage the medical system has left behind. For the most part, once a person becomes accustomed to the oils effects, patients seem to enjoy taking this substance. But due to this medication's non-addictive nature, often those who are using the substance will forget to take their doses properly. It is not that the oil is causing them to forget, it's simply because their bodies do not sense the need for its presence and this only highlights the fact that this medication is truly non-addictive. For if it were not, it's unlikely the patient would forget to take their dosage, because if it were addictive, after eight hours, their bodies would be crying out for the substance.

Are there any side effects one should be concerned about?

Some patients have reported that they experienced anxiety or paranoia with the use of this medication. But complaints such as this usually revolve around the fact that the extract they had been using was not produced in the proper manner or the wrong strain had been used in its production. Another issue concerning the use of this medication which could affect the patient is its unwarranted illegal aspects. Most people do not like the idea of breaking the law and in some cases this can cause patients to have anxiety or paranoia and this will probably continue until all these absurd laws and restrictions have been repealed. The only other side effect I know of about the use of this medication concerns dry mouth, but not all cannabis extracts will cause this. Dry mouth can occur with the use of many powerful medications, but to solve the problem all that is required is to take a drink of water.

The main side effects of hemp oil that have been reported to me are good health, happiness, and a good night's sleep, so what more could anyone ask from a medicine they are using?

Many people ingest a great number of pharmaceuticals every day. Can that be good for the body?

I have no idea why those who see the dangerous side effects of allopathic drugs in TV commercials would still consider taking these medications. It seems that mindlessly many individuals will do as the doctor orders and a good number of these same people tend to reject the use of hemp medicine. Simply because of lies they have been told by their governments and the ones who stand in the shadows behind the pharmaceutical industry.

No one dies from the use of hemp medicine and there is no harm caused. I only wish that I could say the same for what the doctors prescribe to us every day but sadly, that is hardly the case.

Sometimes the different interactions these so-called medications can cause are enough to put us in an early grave. But even if we experience no immediate problems, their use still presents a danger. Over time, the chemicals and poisons these medications contain build up in our bodies and this can also bring about severe problems with our health which can often lead to death. Even simple things like aspirin tablets cause thousands of deaths worldwide every year. So I don't think any of us should put our trust in the pharmaceutical industry or anything they provide. If you wish to see real healing power then turn to Mother Nature, for you will find very little in a pill factory that will be of much benefit.

How do patients compare the side effects of hemp oil to those from chemical medications?

There is no real comparison between the side effects of hemp oil and the poisonous chemicals the medical system provides. Most of these substances which doctors supply are something we should not have in our bodies because they are liver toxic. This means that these so-called medications should not be ingested because they will poison our livers and impair its function. In addition, their use can cause a whole array of other health issues that could be avoided if hemp oil was used instead.

With the use of chemical medications, we often expose ourselves to side effects that can be even worse than what was originally being treated. Many patients with diseases like cancer and diabetes etc. have even told me that their conditions were caused from the medications doctors had been supplying. So it appears that quite often the doctors themselves are at least partially responsible for the patient's current medical situation. Many patients have described to me in detail the horrible side effects they encountered which were caused from the medications they were prescribed, so I would try to avoid the use of pharmaceuticals if at all possible.

Since the chemistry of our bodies and our tolerance for many other substances varies a great deal. Often doctors have no idea what effects a buildup of different chemical medications can have on our health and well-being. No two of us are the same, and different medications mixed together are nothing less than a poisonous chemical cocktail, which in some cases could have completely unexpected consequences health wise for the patient. So how would any doctor be able to factor in all these unknowns to determine what is safe and what is unacceptable?

I honestly think that conditions like Alzheimer's and many other diseases are often caused by the mixture of chemicals their doctors prescribed. Many patients have told me about the problems they encountered with the use of pharmaceuticals, but once they stopped taking these substances and started ingesting these extracts, the problems disappeared. To sum things up bluntly, if hemp medicines are produced properly, they are extremely safe and harmless to use, but what medical professionals provide to us is not.

Is it possible to compare the effects of allopathic and empiric medicine?

As far as I am concerned, there is no comparison between allopathic medicine and empiric medicine. Allopathic medicine is for the most part just a mixture of harmful chemicals and poisons that no one should be ingesting. Empiric medicine (medicine from plants) has been used for thousands of years with good effect and medications produced from cannabis hemp are beyond compare when it comes to safety. The medicinally effective and harmless nature of hemp resins which these extracts are produced from makes the hemp plant the "Queen of all Empiric Medicine."

Throughout the years, I have been in contact with many patients who took everything available to treat their conditions and after all else had failed, they then finally came to me. I think the patients who have used both allopathic and empiric medicine are more qualified to talk about the difference between chemical medications and hemp oil instead of just myself. But sadly many are still too afraid to come forward, so I can only relay what they have reported.

Most of these patients told me directly that they would much sooner use hemp oil rather than the medications their doctors provided. Simply because it worked much better, had no unpleasant side effects, and in a short time, many could go back to living a normal life. They did not experience these pronounced healing effects with the use of allopathic medicines and most felt that these medications were actually doing a great deal of harm. I believe that this speaks volumes as to why I would not even consider the use of allopathic medicines and in the near future I think many more will begin to feel the same.

ANIMALS AND CHILDREN

Before we get into this portion of the book, which deals with the effects these extracts can have on many different serious medical problems. I would like to point out the fact that I receive a great number of emails from individuals who wish to treat small animals and children in the most effective way possible. For some reason or other many of these people tend to believe that due to their size, children and animals should be given much smaller doses. But I completely disagree with this line of thinking, since in reality, properly produced cannabis extracts will do no harm and much the same as an adult, even a child can often build up their tolerance very quickly.

An adult usually requires 60 grams of high quality cannabis extract to bring their bodies back to a state of good health and a child is no different. When one first begins to ingest cannabis extracts those who have a low tolerance will experience a sensation known as becoming high. But since these extracts are not deadly and are also non addictive, why should anyone be concerned if the patient should become somewhat high during the early stages of their treatment? For the first three weeks of treatment while the patient is increasing their dosage, they will experience the sedative effect of this medication and often this will make them somewhat unstable on their feet. But if they simply move slowly and take their time, the sedated sleepy state they are in should be of little concern. As time goes on and the patient's tolerance builds, they will then find that this medication will begin to have no effect on them at all, other than the benefit it is having on their medical problems. So if I had a child who was suffering with a serious condition like cancer, I would treat them no differently than I would treat myself if I was suffering from the same condition.

Animals like dogs do not tend to worry about the effects of this medication, but unfortunately many of their owners seem to believe that too much of this extract could do their pets harm. These extracts promote life and they do not cause death, even if an animal were to ingest a great deal of this medication, they will not be harmed. The animal may sleep for quite some time and when it awakens it may be a bit unsteady on its feet for a short while, but soon the animal will resume its normal behavior. If they still have concerns, an animal owner can follow the dosage instructions I have outlined for humans. But the name of the game it to get the extract into your pet as quickly as possible. So, when treating animals the dosage can be increased much more rapidly and this should give your pet a much better chance to survive. It should also be noted that animals will usually require much less of this extract to heal, when compares to humans. I have often seen animals such as dogs completely healed with the use of only a few grams of these amazing extracts.

CANCER

Judging from observations of the number of patients you have treated, is the oil effective for all types of cancer, or are you aware of any types of cancer that it will not help with?
The oil is effective in the treatment of all types of skin cancers and to the best of my knowledge, the same holds true for internal cancers and other medical conditions as well. After years of experience in dealing with patients who suffered with all types of medical problems. I can honestly say that I do not know of any condition for which the use of these extracts are not of benefit in treating.

High-grade hemp oil, when produced and used according to my instructions, seems to work on all types of cancer and I am not aware of any type of cancer that it would not be effective to treat. Some time ago, I did hear about a study that claimed THC can cause a certain type of cancer, but I think this was just more propaganda that was thrown in to keep the public from learning the truth. I can only say that this study must be flawed and I will now explain why I came to this conclusion.

Put simply, most research tells us cancer is just mutating cells which were allowed to multiply due to an underlying problem present in the patient's body. THC kills mutating cells. So how can THC produce the very cells that it is so good at destroying? One must ask themselves just who would benefit from spreading this false information, to find the answer all you have to do is follow the money.

If you are looking for treatments that can cause cancer, look no further than chemo and radiation. Both of these so-called "treatments" are very carcinogenic, so, in other words, they can and do cause cancer. Even a CT scan exposes the body to a massive dose of radiation. Radiation causes cells to mutate and that is what we have all been told cancer is, mutating cells. Unlike chemotherapy and radiation, the cannabinoids these extracts contain which have proved to be so successful in the treatment of cancer, will not cause our cells to mutate, so how would it be possible then to cause cancer?

Back in the 30s, an amazing man named Royal Rife developed a frequency device, which he used to cure sixteen patients who were suffering from terminal cancer. All this is very well documented, but Rife's efforts to move his invention into mainstream use was blocked by the American Medical Association. According to Rife, it seems he felt that cancer was caused by some form of mutating microbe. Due to all his accomplishments, I think researchers should give his opinions some very serious consideration. There are also others that have claimed cancer is caused by some type of fungus. So it appears that there is no shortage of opinions about the subject. But since we now have an effective treatment for this condition, finding out what causes it is now not of such importance.

If the day ever comes and I have the needed facilities, this is something I would like to look into, for to me it seems that the real cause of cancer is something that has been eluding us for far too long. Possibly Mr. Rife may be correct about his microbe theory, but I would also expect to find many other causes as well, so who knows? Finding a harmless cure for the disease did not prove to be much of a problem, so finding its cause might be more simple than we expect. In time, we may have all the answers.

Can the oil can be used along with chemotherapy and radiation?

When patients ask me this question, I tell them that yes, the oil could be used along with chemo and radiation. I have no doubt the use of this oil would be very beneficial and it would give them a better chance of surviving the effects such treatments cause. Still, why would anyone in their right mind even consider taking chemo and radiation?

Chemo and radiation do not cure cancer, they cause it, and in the past, I have refused to provide oil to people who are planning to take such so-called treatments. Why should I run the risk of going to jail to produce the oil for someone who plans to take treatments such as this from the medical system? If a person chooses to take chemo or radiation, by all means, that is their choice. But from my perspective I feel it would be rather foolish on my part to provide the cure, if these individuals are so intent on letting the medical system poison them. It would be much like supplying an antidote while pumping venom in the patient's veins.

In the past, I have provided this medication to patients who want an effective treatment that does no harm and gives them a very good chance to survive. But I consider most of what the medical system is supplying to be more about murder than it is about medicine. That is the reason I tell people with serious medical conditions to take the oil and stay away from the medical system and their doctors.

Unless medical professionals start behaving rationally towards the treatment of cancer and many other serious conditions, I believe the patient is actually better off by not seeking their advice at all. What the medical system provides in the end usually does much more harm than good and lessens the patient's chance of survival. The damage caused and left behind by chemo and radiation will in most cases bring about the death of the patient, unless they ingest large amounts of oil to detoxify themselves. The vast majority of people who take chemo and radiation die from the effects these treatments cause and not the cancer they were being treated for.

As I said, from my experience, the oil seems to work on all types of cancer, but I have had a few people who acquired the treatment and then refused to take it. I cannot explain their behavior other than to say that in the end it seems they were unwilling to break with the medical system. There have only been a few who have done this and, as far as I know, in the end all these patients died. I wish that I could explain why people do the things they do and why they are so reckless with their lives. But unless they are willing to educate themselves about what the medical system has in store for them I expect that this will continue.

What is the success rate for cancer patients?

When people come to me with a diagnosis of cancer and they have refused to take chemotherapy or radiation their success rate is very high unless they have waited until they are at death's door to take the treatment, or they refuse to ingest the oil in the proper way.

Cancer can even be reversed in roughly 75% of those who have been badly damaged by the medical system if they take the oil treatment properly. However, there are about 1 in 4 who have been so badly damaged the best one can hope for is to give them a much better quality of life while they are still with us. But for patients in this situation, ingesting the oil still makes good sense, for it will ease their suffering a great deal and often they will live on much longer than expected.

Even if you can cure the cancer, in the end the damage from the chemo and radiation will often bring about the patient's death unless the harm that was caused can be repaired. These individuals are not dying from cancer; they are in fact dying from the so-called "medical treatments" they received from the medical system. As you can see, hemp oil does have an amazing success rate especially when no doctors are involved. But if the medical system would start behaving rationally and use this medication as they should, I think survival rates could increase even more.

How many people that you know of have cured themselves with the oil?

Since 2003, I have provided these extracts to roughly 5,000 people who were suffering with all types of medical problems. Many of these patients had several medical issues which needed attention but most were brought under control or cured with the use of this oil. Due to the illegal status of this medication, I did not keep records, but it's safe to say I have seen thousands of people cured with external and internal cancers, plus a great number of other conditions.

In addition, I receive vast numbers of e-mails every week from all over the world, telling me how much this oil has helped patients in faraway lands. When we put the instructions on our website and brought out the documentary "Run From the Cure", explaining to individuals everywhere how they can heal themselves, it drew a lot of attention and many used this information to help provide those in need with a medication that worked. Since this oil is so easy to produce, already untold numbers of people worldwide have experienced its benefits and it is my hope that in the near future we will all have the freedom to do the same.

Is it ever too late to start using the oil?

It's never too late to start using this amazing medication. Even people who have been badly damaged by the medical system still have a good chance of making a recovery. We had one gentleman with lung cancer who was in the hospital and doctors had given him twenty-four hours to live. Despite opposition from the medical system, his son gave him a large dose of oil and he left the hospital the very next day. About fifteen months later, this 83-year-old veteran did die, but not from lung cancer, he passed away due to a pre-existing heart condition that he had suffered from for years. During the extra months that he had lived, he enjoyed a good quality of life and he died in his sleep with no pain. Isn't that better than dying in a hospital, drowning in your own fluid from lung cancer?

We have had great results in the treatment of those who have stage 4 cancers and were not expected to live. Of course, we could not save them all, but one thing is for certain, we did save many more than the medical system could with their insane treatments and dismal survival rates. As I stated earlier, this oil is effective in the treatment of all types of cancer but the results I often witnessed in those suffering from lung cancer and leukemia were truly astounding. Frequently, these types of cancers respond very dramatically to the oil treatment and it is not unusual for patients to see improvements in their conditions daily.

I always encourage those who are taking the oil to get it into their system as quickly as possible. The idea is the faster they can ingest the THC-laden oil into their bodies, the more quickly they can cure their cancer and other conditions. This will ensure that the patient has a much better chance to survive, but still they will not be harmed.

I tell everyone with serious life-threatening conditions, "The oil will either save your life, or it will ease your way out." Even if the patient does pass away, they will do so with dignity and the effects of all those horrible pain medications can be avoided. Our aim is to save as many as we can, but for those beyond help, it's still nice to know that they will not have to go through a painful agonizing death, like others with the same conditions must endure in hospitals.

Are some people more difficult to cure than others?

People who are the hardest to cure are the ones who have allowed themselves to be severely damaged by the medical system. Chemotherapy and radiation are both carcinogenic treatments, in other words they cause cancer. If the patient can survive these so-called treatments, they may witness a reduction in the size of a tumor and in some cases the cancer may appear to be completely gone. But in the end these treatments poison the body so badly that they are left with no immune system to protect them. This in conjunction with the cancer-causing effects of these treatments themselves helps to spread the cancer to other places in the body.

Since the patient no longer has an immune system which functions properly to protect them, they are incapable of defending themselves against many minor medical problems which now can bring about their death. Any rational person should have no trouble understanding why the treatments provided by the medical system do not work. Yet, doctors continue to tell us that there are no other forms of effective treatment available. I guess this just highlights the fact that if you pay doctors and other professionals enough money to not understand something, in most cases they are happy to comply.

I must also mention the fact that quite often patients are already taking medications that block their cannabinoid receptors, or interfere with the function of the endocannabinoid system. Such medications include *Remonabant*, *Surinabant*, *Taranabant*, and *Ibipenabant*, just to name a few. Since it was the doctors who prescribed these substances in the first place, I feel this is something that should be discussed with them. This is one of the reasons I tell patients to get off the chemical medications as soon as possible. If the function of your cannabinoid receptors is impaired, it makes such people much more difficult or impossible to treat.

Many individuals today seem to think the power of our minds has a lot to do with recovering from serious illnesses. They often feel certain that a positive attitude and a strong belief in the treatment being used is very important when it comes to healing. But most of those who came to me did not believe when they began treatment that this oil would be of any benefit. So although I agree that the power of positive thinking could be helpful, the vast majority of those I treated seemed to be able to heal quite nicely without it.

I tend to look at healing successfully as having more to do with the proper medication being used, rather than the state of a patient's mind. I expect that many who believe in this new age rhetoric will tend to disagree, but I have no reason to twist the facts about what I have witnessed. In addition, our pets and other animal life have cannabinoid receptors in their bodies as well so they too can benefit from the effects of this oil. I have treated many animals and although some of these creatures were quite intelligent, I am sure the miracles this oil produced had nothing to do with positive thinking.

TREATING SKIN CANCER

If the oil is produced properly, it will definitely work to cure skin cancer and it usually only takes a small amount of oil to accomplish the task. Apply the oil to the area that is causing the problem and cover it with a bandage, then reapply fresh oil and a new bandage every three or four days and the cancer should soon disappear.

I always tell patients to continue treatment until the cancer is gone and then continue to treat the area for about two more weeks just as if the cancer was still there. Doing this will ensure that all the cancer cells are dead and I have never seen a skin cancer return if my instructions are followed.

If you have had skin cancer for quite some time and the cancer is well established, it may take quite a while to cure, but usually even in quite severe cases, skin cancer will disappear in less than a month. In an extreme case, it may take longer, but if so, then just keep up the treatment until it is completely healed. Many people can cure their skin cancer in no time, but it all depends on your own rate of healing and how deeply embedded the cancer has become.

How many people have cured skin cancer using your hemp oil?

I have provided the oil to hundreds of people with skin cancers. Usually within three weeks, the cancer is gone and all that remains is healthy pink skin. I really cannot give you an estimate of how many patients worldwide have used my method of treatment to cure such cancers. Yet, since this treatment is becoming so well known, I expect that by this time, hundreds of thousands, if not millions, worldwide have cured themselves of this condition in this manner.

Can you compare this treatment to standard procedures?

There is no comparison between treating skin cancers with hemp oil and what the medical system tends to call proper treatment. Quite often surgery is performed and sometimes they are successful in removing all the cancer cells that are present. But judging from those I have met, who had to return over and over again to have it removed, I would say that this is quite rare. In far too many cases, patients must return to their doctors to have these operations repeated again and again.

Even when these operations are performed several times, the medical system often fails to eradicate the problem. Doctors also use other treatments for skin cancers, such as liquid nitrogen and creams containing chemo. These treatments are usually painful and, in many cases, the cancer just keeps coming back and tends to get much worse.

When hemp oil is used to treat skin cancer, it kills only the mutating cancer cells and the condition usually heals quickly. This harmless effective treatment causes no harm to healthy cells and from my experience, I believe that it is by far the most sensible way to treat this condition. Methods used by the medical system are to say the least unpleasant by comparison and one does not have to worry about infections or other complications when these extracts are used.

Would you describe how THC acts on cancer cells versus healthy cells?

First of all, THC does not harm healthy cells but it can have devastating effects on cells which have become cancerous. Most individuals have little knowledge about how these cells behave but in reality cancer cells are actually trying to commit suicide and this is a well-documented fact. But if our immune system has become compromised, we cannot produce enough natural cannabinoids to put a stop to their growth. When cells become cancerous, they actually produce more cannabinoid receptors, which allows the natural cannabinoids that our bodies produce to enter more readily. These same receptors will also accept cannabinoids like THC that the hemp plant produces and this can be of great benefit to the patient. So if your body is not producing enough of these natural substances to stop the cancer's growth, then we must look for another way to bring up the cannabinoid levels in our bodies to fight off the disease.

By ingesting hemp oil, it provides these cannabinoids in abundance and then the disease can often be brought under control and cured. Our bodies produce cancer cells every day, so in essence we all have cancer but if our immune system is functioning properly, these cells pose little or no danger to our well-being. When our immune systems become impaired, often that is when cancer will make its presence known. But if a person is wise enough to ingest hemp oil to give their immune systems a boost instead of going to the medical system, its presence will not usually be felt for long.

We have studied research papers on the subject and I will now give you the scientific explanation as to why THC is effective in the treatment of cancer. When hemp oil is ingested as a cancer medication, the THC in the oil causes a buildup of a fat molecule called ceramide. When ceramide comes in contact with cancer cells, it causes programmed cell death, while doing no harm to healthy cells. This is the way it was explained in the scientific research we have studied but I have never stopped looking for other explanations as well.

With the help of a wonderful lady named Batya Stark, I have developed a new theory which involves our pineal gland and the melatonin it produces. Fluoride and many of the chemicals doctors provide plus other things we come into contact with, often impairs the ability of the pineal gland to produce melatonin. Melatonin is the greatest antioxidant known to man and it travels to every cell in our bodies. The pineal gland and the melatonin it produces can play a very dramatic role in maintaining good health and indeed has a lot to do with our overall sense of well-being.

With the function of the pineal gland impaired, its ability to produce melatonin is greatly diminished. It has been found that as we age, melatonin levels decrease, and I feel this reduction could also have an effect on the development of cancer. It has been scientifically proven that just smoking hemp can raise melatonin levels a great deal. Perhaps this is one of the reasons why individuals who smoke hemp have lower cancer rates than those who don't. Now just think of what ingesting the raw unburned oil would do for your melatonin levels.

From what I can understand, cannabinoids in the oil causes the pineal gland to go into overdrive and subsequently melatonin levels sharply increase. This, at least in part, is what we think causes the wonderful effect this medication has on so many conditions including cancer. If the pineal gland is producing vast amounts of melatonin, it does no harm to the body, but it can have a devastating effect on the disease the patient is suffering from. When melatonin levels remain high, the illness or disease that has been plaguing the patient can often be brought under control or even completely cured. In reality, I am not a doctor nor do I have the qualifications necessary to become one, but I still feel we should leave our minds open to other explanations. If I am correct about the importance of melatonin, then it may give us a new way of looking at disease control and it could help to explain the anti-aging effects this medication produces.

SKIN CONDITIONS

From my experience with our currently banned hemp cosmetics, in which we used oil from industrial hemp buds, which is much weaker when compared to the oil you make, we found hemp is basically a cure-all because it can be used on almost any condition. Can you confirm this?

History calls hemp a panacea, which means cure-all and in the past it was used to treat a vast array of medical problems. From my experience in seeing hemp oil used for various medical conditions, I too call hemp a cure-all. Hemp is useful in the treatment of practically any disease or condition; it promotes full-body healing without doing any harm. So to me and many others, this has become the ultimate medicine and I firmly believe that there is nothing better.

In the world we live in today, many are even afraid to go out in the sun but this medication mixes well with such things as skin creams and suntan lotion, so why hide in the dark? Wouldn't it be nice to go out in the sun again and enjoy life without worrying about things like skin cancer? You bet it would and now this wonderful substance can make this all possible.

LEUKEMIA

If you treat someone who has leukemia with hemp oil, it often produces results very quickly. Leukemia, from my experience, is one of the easiest internal cancers to cure and we have seen spectacular results with this oil's use. The first place THC goes after entering the body is directly into the bloodstream. If cancer is present in the blood, it will not likely be present for long. I have seen the white blood cell count in those suffering from leukemia come down dramatically in two days and in my opinion, I feel that there is no better treatment for those who suffer with this condition.

DIABETES

Diabetics that have just been diagnosed are usually quite easy to cure and in no time they are often free of the disease. But in patients who have had this condition for a long time and have suffered the effects of the disease for years, it will often take longer. Even in badly damaged patients, if high-quality oil is taken properly, often within six weeks they no longer need insulin. Unfortunately, the damage this disease causes within our bodies can take considerably longer to heal, but given time, most of this too can be repaired.

The oil seems to often have the ability to rejuvenate the pancreas quite rapidly, so it can again function properly. We were first able to prove this on a diabetic I had treated for cancer. At the end of his cancer treatment, he went off the oil completely for ten days. To my surprise, his blood sugar levels remained normal and he was eating many things that a diabetic should not. This man had been a diabetic for over thirty years and he had been taking two injections of insulin a day. So after he had taken no oil for ten days and his blood sugar levels remained normal it became obvious that his pancreas must be functioning properly again to at least some degree.

I always tell patients I am not a doctor, but I think it would be in their best interests if they could get off the chemical medications they are using for other conditions. Quite often, certain medications can impede the oil treatment's effectiveness and the oil's use will usually replace these medications anyway.

I have had reports from patients who were suffering from both type 1 and type 2 diabetes that stated the oil had treated them successfully. For instance, I have encountered patients who have been injecting insulin for thirty years or more, and, after starting the oil, within six weeks they no longer needed to take these injections. At the same time, other reports I received from some stated they were only successful in lowering their insulin intake. But they also stated that with the use of the oil it also did other wonderful things that improved their overall health.

The way I look at it, getting off insulin and having the pancreas controlling blood sugar levels once more is the goal. Yet, even if this cannot be completely accomplished, the effects of the oil will still be very beneficial to the patient's body. Since this disease causes circulation problems and other complications, often an infection caused from an injury is impossible to heal using the medical systems so-called conventional methods. For example, if a diabetic gets an infection on their foot and it refuses to heal properly, in the end, the medical system's answer is to remove the foot or at least the part that had become infected.

I have known of diabetics personally who had this done and in no time they usually need to have more removed because the infection continues to spread. What a horrible prospect for a diabetic to face and what makes it even worse is the fact that these operations are completely unnecessary and only serve to cripple the patient.

At that time, I knew nothing about the healing abilities of the hemp plant and all I could do was watch the agony these patients had to go through; but since then I have finally learned the truth. If the oil is used externally, it will heal diabetic ulcers in a very short time, so you can just imagine the benefits a diabetic receives when this substance is ingested. I have been making this information available for years but still doctors choose to ignore the use of this medication and continue to mutilate their patients. This is one of the reasons that I have no use for the medical system and all these so-called doctors who feed off our suffering.

After taking the oil treatment, many diabetics who have been on re-stricted diets for years behave like a kid in a candy store. Suddenly, they can again eat foods that a diabetic should not and some patients will tend to overindulge themselves. As time goes on, the oil can reverse damage that has been done to the bodies of diabetics such as bad circulation, etc. The oil will also heal those nasty infections that diabetics have to deal with in a sensible way, and from what we have witnessed, high-grade hemp oil is effective in the treatment of all types of diabetes.

INFECTIONS

If this oil can heal infections for diabetics, it almost goes without saying that this medication is very effective to treat infections of all kinds. All you have to do is apply oil to the infection, the same as you would if you were treating skin cancer. In a short time, the oil should take care of the infec-tion and it will simply disappear. When you treat a diabetic ulcer or other serious infection, you will see the infected wound begin to shrink. The size of the wound will continue to become smaller and smaller until only a tiny hole is left. Of course while this is taking place, poison will continue to drain from the area into the bandage and there will likely be some dead white skin around the wound itself. Do not be alarmed; this is all just part of the healing process. Another thing that may surprise you is that the bandage can be removed with little or no pain at all, because these extracts will not allow the bandage to stick to the wound.

Then finally, after all the poison has drained itself from the area being treated, the small hole itself will heal over and disappear. As time goes on, the area where the wound had existed will blend in with the surrounding skin.

Hemp oil does have a reputation for leaving no scars after healing, so don't be surprised if the day comes that you cannot find where the wound was yourself. This oil is a natural antibiotic and a natural anesthetic, so I can think of nothing better to treat painful wounds, burns, and infections. We have even used the oil to successfully treat flesh-eating disease, so if these extracts can cure this horrible condition, I firmly believe that there is little it cannot.

INFLAMMATIONS, ARTHRITIS

Arthritis is caused by inflammation, usually accompanied by swelling and in most cases a great deal of pain. But the greatest natural anti-inflammatory on earth usually has little trouble in dealing with this condition. Relieving inflammation is one of hemp's oldest medicinal uses and it is known to be a very effective treatment for this condition in people of all ages. Many varieties of hemp produce oils that are very effective in treating those suffering from this debilitating and painful disease. I have supplied oil to a great number of patients with this condition and even those with rheumatoid arthritis have found there is nothing better to ease their suffering.

I was contacted by a lady in England who reported that with the use of this substance, she had cured her rheumatoid arthritis in nine weeks. To the best of my knowledge, this form of arthritis is one of the worst, so if this natural oil can take the swelling away and cure the condition, I expect that it can do the same for any form of this disease.

Patients who have arthritis are given harmful and addictive pain medications that do nothing more than mask the pain. The use of these medications can cause the patient to have many unpleasant side-effects such as stomach problems and constipation, etc. The use of hemp oil does not present such problems, so if you have arthritis do yourself a favor and start using something that is harmless and effective.

CHRONIC PAIN

If you have the proper varieties to make the oil from, there is nothing better for chronic pain relief than hemp oil. The oils from many types of hemp are a wonderful natural painkiller which is not addictive or harmful. The medical system gives chronic pain sufferers dangerous, addictive, and harmful medications to control their pain. I do admit that such medications are somewhat effective but essentially all they do is mask the pain while providing no healing effect. When you are taking hemp oil for chronic pain, it not only reduces the pain, it actually goes to work trying to heal the cause of your suffering. For anyone suffering from chronic pain, hemp oil is by far the best treatment, since it is non-addictive and does no harm to the rest of your body.

I have seen people with bone cancer in agony when morphine and all the other pain medications the medical system uses could not kill their pain. But the hemp oil brought their pain under control in a matter of hours and they were able to get off these harmful substances very quickly with very few withdrawal symptoms. I have also provided this medication to many patients with chronic pain and some of the results have been truly amazing. It was not unusual for me to receive reports from patients the very next day, telling me that they are no longer suffering.

As I said, hemp oil has the ability to eliminate pain, but it also goes to work healing the cause. Again, the idea is to get off these dangerous addictive pharmaceutical medications as quickly as possible and replace them with the use of this oil. Realistically, there is no comparison between hemp oil and pharmaceuticals. Most pain medications supplied by our medical system are dangerous, addictive, and deadly, while hemp oil presents no addiction or danger to the patient.

If a patient is taking morphine or other opiates to control their pain, I suggest they begin with doses about the size of a piece of short-grained dry rice. Then increase the amount you are ingesting as rapidly as possible, while reducing your intake of other medications until you have no further need for the pharmaceuticals at all. There are vast numbers of people who have been taking medications that their doctors prescribed for years and they have done little or nothing to help. If you want to know what it's like to feel good again, give the oil a try and leave the insanity of the medical system behind.

BACK PAIN, SCOLIOSIS

Have you had any patients that experienced relief from back pain or scoliosis?

The producer of our documentary "Run from the Cure" Christian Laurette had suffered with scoliosis for years. About thirteen years ago, the medical system offered to do an operation but they would only give Christian a 50/50 chance of walking again. With odds like this, he felt his only alternative was to live with the pain. Almost daily, he would collapse in agony from the scoliosis and he had more or less convinced himself that nothing could help. I provided him with some hemp oil and within hours he reported that he experienced no further back pain.

I explained to him that he had lived his life with a condition that would not allow him to exercise the way a normal person should, therefore his back muscles were very weak. As expected, after taking the oil as directed, Christian now functions normally with no pain, his back muscles have strengthened and he can now go without the oil for extended periods. Christian is just one of many with back problems who have found an effective cure or control with the use of this medication to ease their discomfort. In my opinion, there is no need for anyone to go through life in a constant state of agony. If you have back problems of any nature, I am sure this medication's use will be of great benefit for most who have these conditions.

MULTIPLE SCLEROSIS (MS)

What are your experiences with curing multiple sclerosis? Many people already know that hemp can help, but do not know how to use it.

Recently we received a report from a lady suffering with MS who ingested two ounces of high-grade hemp oil a year ago for her condition. The effect of the oil treatment was very successful and even though she has ingested no oil over the last year, she remains in good health. From my experience, multiple sclerosis is often curable, but for people who have suffered for years with this condition, it will take time to undo the damage the disease has caused. Many MS sufferers smoke hemp for relief, but using hemp in this manner will not cure them and the disease will continue to progress.

The only way I know to treat MS and the damage associated with this disease effectively is to ingest the oil on a regular basis until it is cured or brought under control. If you have MS, do yourself a favor and give this medication a try. Life is supposed to be about living, not suffering, so why should a patient allow this condition to ruin their life when it can be treated in an effective manner? I know of many patients with this disorder who could no longer walk properly, but after only a few weeks of ingesting the oil, they could again walk normally. MS is just one of many conditions that doctors say cannot be cured, instead they tell us that they can only manage the symptoms, while the disease itself continues to take its toll. If you would like to prove your doctor wrong, give the oil a try and start living for a change and when you do, I am sure you will realize that the guy in the white coat does not always have all the answers.

BURNS

I know from personal experience that there is no better treatment for severe burns than hemp oil. If oil is applied to a burn, it takes the pain away within minutes and greatly accelerates the healing process. If hospitals would use hemp oil in their burn units, human suffering could be greatly reduced.

Back when I first started producing the oil, I was ingesting many harmful medications prescribed by doctors which affected my reasoning abilities, so my thinking was not very clear. This altered state caused me to be somewhat careless and this resulted in an explosion and fire, which left my right hand with severe third degree burns.

When I say severe, I mean severe, three quarters of my right hand had literally melted and was now hanging in gobs. My then girlfriend Leah came down and after she looked at the burn, she took a pair of scissors and cut off all the dead flesh. I know this sounds gruesome, but what she removed was dead, so in reality I did not feel a thing.

In eleven days, my hand was completely healed, leaving no scars. The only way you could tell that I had even sustained an injury, was the presence of all the new pink skin that was visible and even the hair follicles grew back.

Now look what goes on in these burn units that our medical system provides. Children and adults which have endured severe burns will find that burn units are little more than torture chambers, which seem to provide no end to the suffering. These patients are subject to infections, many painful operations involving skin grafts and in the end, they are usually still badly scarred.

The essential oil of the hemp plant is a natural anesthetic and a natural anti-biotic. When you put the oil from the hemp plant right on a burn, within 5 minutes the pain is gone and the healing begins. Judging from what I have seen this substance do to heal the burn I sustained and others who have suffered similar injuries, I firmly believe that this amazing medication could possibly re-grow the face or other parts of the body for those who have suffered a severe burn.

If the oil can re-grow my hand and leave no scars, then why not a foot, or even a face? So, if those who run burn units would really like to help their patients and ease their suffering, perhaps it's just about time that they started using something that works.

SCARS

I have seen burns healed with the use of this oil that should have left horrible scars behind. But afterwards, all that remained was healthy pink skin and according to the medical system such things should not be possible. Throughout history, hemp has always had a reputation for having the ability to heal wounds while leaving little or no scarring afterwards.

I have supplied this oil to many people who had bad complexions and scarring problems on their faces. After treatment with the oil, the improvement in their complexions was astounding. Even scars which have been there for years can be completely or for the most part removed simply by treating the affected area with oil.

This can be accomplished in much the same way that one would treat a skin cancer: simply apply the oil to the scar, and cover with a bandage. Keep repeating this until the scar fades away and in time, the area that was treated will blend in with the surrounding tissue.

I came into contact with a man in the Czech Republic who had a horrible scar on his face which looked like it had been caused by a sword. After he treated the area with oil, I had a very hard time even telling where the scar had been. From my perspective, those who have been disfigured by scaring can be helped and the treatment is painless, so if you have a nasty scar, now you know how to deal with it.

ULCERS, WARTS, MOLES

Ulcers within the body can be cured by ingesting these extracts. Unhealthy ulcers, warts, and moles on the body can be removed by simply applying oil and covering them with a bandage. The oil goes after unhealthy or mutating cells and destroys them painlessly in most cases. Quite often, warts and moles can become unhealthy, at which time they will usually darken in color and begin to grow. If you have something like this to deal with, doctors can often remove the problem, but in many cases, it just

To rid the body of such things in a sensible way, give this medi-
ʌ try.

ʌɪ the past, I have even treated people who were suffering with plantar
warts on their feet and this type of wart develops large roots, which usually
can only be eradicated by an extensive operation. Rather than let the medical system cut your feet to ribbons, simply apply a drop of oil to the head
of the wart and cover it with a bandage. Try to keep the bandage in place
for about three days, then reapply the oil and another bandage. Usually
after doing this three to four times, the roots of the wart have been destroyed and the head of the wart itself just falls off. When the oil is used
to treat this condition, all this takes place painlessly, so if you are suffering
with planter's warts, why go through the torture that the medical system
has in mind for you, heal yourself in a sensible way instead.

MIGRAINES

Patients have found the oil very effective in reducing the frequency of
their migraine headaches and in many cases eliminating them altogether.
The most effective way to treat migraines is to ingest the oil or use it in
suppository form, but even smoking hemp may be of value to someone
who has this condition. In addition, some patients have claimed that they
can get relief by simply applying a small amount of oil topically, but I feel
ingesting the oil or using it in suppository form is far more effective. Migraines can be very hard to live with and what the doctors provide usually
has limited benefits. In many cases these medications can do more harm
than good and if possible I think their use should be avoided by using
something natural. If I was suffering from migraines, I know what I would
be taking and I hope all who suffer these dreadful headaches have the
common sense to do the same.

ASTHMA

Even smoking cannabis is beneficial for many asthma sufferers, but ingesting the oil or vaporizing it is a much more effective and medicinal way
to treat this condition. Using the oil in suppository form is also very effective for those with breathing problems, and so this method could be of
benefit as well. We know many people who have asthma that have been
helped with the use of this medication and I can honestly say that I am

not aware of any treatment for this condition that is more effective. Even those who suffer from such things as COPD have witnessed amazing improvements in their ability to breath properly with the use of this medication. If you are experiencing any type of breathing problems, give the oil a try and I am sure you will have no regrets.

ANXIETY, PARANOIA

I think anxiety and paranoia with the use of this medicine could be greatly reduced if the system would simply stop arresting people for using it. When beginning treatment with the oil, I tell patients, "If the oil is making you sleepy, don't fight it."

Some people can become anxious while trying to overcome the relaxing effect of this medication when what they really should do is just relax and not fight these effects. Many varieties of hemp have a very low potential to cause anxiety, but there are some strains which do. If patients feel uncomfortable with the oil they are trying to use in such cases, I often advise them to produce the medicine from a strain that will cause less problems.

If this medicine's use were only legal, I am sure it would take away much of the anxiety associated with its use. Also some strains can produce more anxiety than others, so if you are experiencing such feelings, simply switching strains could eliminate the problem. Many people find using substances like dark chocolate and cayenne pepper to be quite effective in helping to lower their anxiety and reduce their heart rate. The most important thing to remember with the use of this medication is to keep in mind that it is the safest medicine on earth.

The use of this substance does no harm and if the patient experiences anxiety, it is caused quite frequently by the patients themselves because they get all worked up for no reason. Or often pharmaceutical drugs that a patient is needlessly trying to ingest could present a problem which can give them symptoms of anxiety. But this is easily rectified in most cases by simply getting off these harmful chemical medications. In addition there is also a natural substance which our bodies produce called *citicoline* that is supposed to be effective to treat anxiety as well. I am told that *citicoline* is available in 70 countries, so if you just go on the internet, you should have little trouble locating what you require.

It takes a while to get used to hemp oil's effects and beginners may experience some anxiety. But in a short time, most will become comfortable with its use and the anxiety will just fade away. As a matter of fact, once patients become accustomed to the oil's effects, they often laugh about the way it had scared them so badly in the beginning.

Quite frequently, I am still contacted by patients who tried to use a sativa strain to produce their medication and often the effects of a strong sativa can cause a great deal of anxiety. This continues to happen even though I have stated many times such strains should not be used because they are too energizing.

You don't want a patient to be energized, you need to use a strong sedative Indica to help him or her to relax and heal while sleeping. I hate to see people waste their time and money trying to produce oil from the wrong strains, but that is often what happens when our instructions are not followed. With a little effort, I am sure we can develop good medicinal varieties that will produce no anxiety at all. But this cannot be accomplished in the proper way until we have the freedom to do the simple research that is required.

DEPRESSION

I have found both sativa and indica strains to be effective in the treatment of depression. Yet, I seldom use sativa strains for treating patients due to their energizing effects. Most patients who come to me are suffering from a serious illness and I don't want them energized during the healing process.

I find the sleep and rest that a good indica extracts provides to be the most beneficial for the vast majority of medical conditions. Oil from a good indica variety is very effective in the treatment of depression and can often eliminate this problem in a very short time. Most who have come to me were in a depressed state due to other conditions they were suffering from. When the condition is cured or brought under control, the depressed state they were experiencing just fades away.

INSOMNIA

As for insomnia, there is nothing better than properly produced oil from a good indica strain to give a person the sleep they require. The effects of my head injury left me with what can best be described as a tuning fork gone mad inside my head. This high-pitched sound made it impossible for me to sleep and I was unable to get the rest I required. The medical system gave me many different medications to treat this condition but nothing worked. In addition, I was often left with terrible side effects from the use of these drugs which caused me more distress than the condition I suffer from.

I found that just smoking cannabis allowed me to get more rest than any of the other medication the medical system had provided. Then when I started ingesting hemp oil, I received even more relief and it was not unusual for me to obtain eight to twelve hours of uninterrupted sleep.

For years before ingesting these extracts, I would get up more tired than when I had gone to bed and I was getting very little rest at night. Then all of a sudden after taking the oil I started waking up in the morning well rested and refreshed.

As many of us get older, we start experiencing sleeping problems and this can have a very detrimental effect on our overall health and well-being. The doctors can give you sleeping pills, but if you really knew what they were made from and the danger they can present, I doubt that you would want them in your body.

A good night's sleep is not something that is just nice to have, it's a necessity if you want to remain active and healthy and there is nothing better than hemp oil to give your body the rest you require.

VITAL ORGANS

A great number of people who have taken these extracts have reported improvements in the function of many vital organs. From our experience, it seems that hemp oil can rejuvenate all vital organs within our bodies and bring them back to a much more healthy state over the years. We have seen kidney, lung, liver, pancreas, and heart functions, etc. greatly improve for many patients. Indeed, we have even seen massive improvements in brain function for those who suffer from Alzheimer's disease and I think that one could only consider their brain as being a vital organ also. Although, those who stand against the use of hemp medicine seem to be able to function quite well without the use of one.

Doctors are kept very busy these days doing organ transplants, then the patient must stay on anti-rejection drugs so their body will not reject the transplanted organ. Since we have a medication that can rejuvenate vital organs, shouldn't we be using it to do just that? It may make things a bit slow in operating rooms, but I think that it makes much more sense for the patient to rejuvenate their own organs if possible rather than go under the knife and have to take anti-rejection drugs for the rest of their lives. When the medical system and the public finally wake up, I am sure all this will come to pass. In the meantime, if you are having problems with one of your vital organs, do something about it, start ingesting the oil and save yourself a lot of grief.

BODY WEIGHT REGULATION, DETOXIFICATION

Hemp oil is a great detoxifier and it is not unusual for people who are overweight to lose many pounds during their treatment. It's almost as if the oil knows what you should weigh and over time it will bring your body to that level. In my own case, the oil took about 30 pounds off me, but I have seen many patients lose a great deal more.

When you are ingesting hemp oil, it is not like being on a diet. You can eat as much as you want to and whatever you like. The oil seems to naturally curb an overweight person's appetite and I know of no better or safer way to lose weight. In addition, it can also stimulate the appetite of a person who needs to gain weight.

It's just as I said, the oil wants to bring your body back to a healthy weight no matter if you are underweight or overweight. If you would like to go on some type of diet, that is your choice, but I for one would prefer not to eat rabbit food all the time to maintain good health.

In addition, at my age I really find no joy in doing all kinds of exercises, so if I wanted to lose weight this would not be an option. If I want to shed a few pounds, I know the way to do it without diets or exercise and now you are also aware of how this can be accomplished yourself. Once this wonderful oil becomes more available, in a short time, those who are now overweight or underweight will likely not remain so for long. Being overweight can cause an early death, so if you are carrying a few pounds extra, now you know how to deal with the problem.

Do you mean it seriously that it can take off excess weight without exercise?

Yes, hemp oil can take weight off without exercise and I am living proof. If I take my shirt off, I look like someone who has worked out a great deal and my body is at the correct weight for a man of my height.

When I was younger, I did a lot of swimming, but now since losing the excess weight I was carrying, you can see all of my stomach muscles again. I don't even have love handles, just a band of muscle on each side and I don't do any exercises. If you would like to experience the same, all you have to do is follow my example and soon your body will begin to look the way it should.

PSORIASIS

I know of no better treatment for psoriasis than hemp oil. Psoriasis comes from within the body and this condition can best be corrected by ingesting the oil. For psoriasis sufferers, I provide oil to ingest and in addition I often supply a cannabis tincture or some extra raw oil itself to treat their psoriasis externally. I have even seen many people get great results who have only used the oil or tincture topically for their psoriasis. But I still think that ingesting the oil is by far the best, since it heals the underlying condition which is causing the problem. For some people with less severe psoriasis, just a few applications of hemp oil topically can often heal them and quite frequently, the psoriasis does not return. The medical system does supply things like coal tar treatments which can have short-range benefits, but the psoriasis just comes back. Often individuals who have severe forms of this condition will hide themselves away because they are so self-conscious about their appearance. Rather than let this condition ruin your life, start using something that works and I am sure you will soon begin to feel much better about yourself.

AIDS

A guy in a YouTube video describes his positive experience with alleviating the symptoms of AIDS. Could you tell us more about that?
Shawn, the man who has quite a few video clips up on YouTube, had suffered from AIDS for twenty years. He started ingesting the oil for his condition after listening to me speak on Jack Herer's Internet show. At the time he was in very bad shape and he was going to purchase a walker

to help him get around. Within a month, Shawn reduced his intake of pharmaceutical medications from thirty-six pills a day down to ten and he was out jogging rather than looking for a walker. When I last spoke to him, he was only ingesting the oil and he was off all the other medications. He was carrying a zero viral load and if this continues, the system will have to declare that his AIDS is cured or at least it is well under control.

The medical community says they have no effective treatment for this condition, so they just fill those who are suffering with AIDS, full of chemical medications and antibiotics, then watch the patient slowly die. As far as I am concerned, this disease is just another cash cow for the drug companies to make a big profit from. The patients do the suffering and dying, while the drug companies fill their pockets by supplying what they call medications. When you look at the devastation this disease is causing in counties such as Africa, one can only wonder about how much longer this can go on.

For those who are currently suffering from this horrible disease, the good news is that help is on the way and it comes in the form of extracts from the cannabis hemp plant. But the bad news is that those who need it most cannot obtain this oil legally, until we can rid ourselves of all the corruption which stands in the way of this medicinal plant's free use. People are dying and, from my perspective, any government which is denying their citizens the use of this oil to heal themselves are guilty of outright murder against their own countrymen. At present, it truly is a sad situation, but in the near future, the people will have their medicine and no government or their rich masters who stand in the shadows will be able to do anything to stop them.

AUTISM, MENTAL DISORDERS

Has anyone tried hemp oil for autism or other mental diseases?

I have no experience with autistic patients but I think hemp oil would be very effective in treating this condition and I have received reports to that effect. I know people who have given their children hemp to treat the imaginary disorder called ADHD with great success. When I was in school, there was no such thing as ADHD, children that showed signs of restlessness were simply said to be overactive. Now they are trying to make us believe that it is something which must be treated. Well, if this is actually so, then I would treat my child with hemp oil, for at least I would then know that they will not be harmed.

The standard treatment for ADHD involves chemical drugs like Ritalin and no one seems to be sure what long term effects medications like this can have. What would you like to see your own child take, chemicals that can have unknown effects on the child for years to come or hemp oil which is natural and does no harm?

I have also supplied oil to people suffering from bipolar disorder and schizophrenia with good results and I believe that this medication would be beneficial for most if not all mental disorders. The first thing parents should know about autism is that often it is caused by the shots and vaccinations our children are given after birth. Go on the Internet and look up Dr. Rebecca Carley and watch her documentary "Vaccines, The New Weapons of Mass Destruction" and that should answer your questions.

Hemp oil detoxifies the body, so it could also very well rid a child's body of the harmful substances vaccines contain. If you have a child that is autistic, why not give them a chance to have a normal life by allowing them to take doses of oil for a few weeks? The oil is harmless and if it can help to heal a child's mental issues caused from the toxins which were injected, why not give it a try? The medical system has no rational treatments available to effectively treat mental disturbances. The drugs they use often present a danger to the individuals who are taking these substances and others around them. When we hear about young people going into schools and shooting their classmates, check into the medications they were taking and you will probably find the cause. In many of these cases, the chemical drugs supplied by the system do more harm than good and often with the use of such drugs, patients can act strangely or even become suicidal. Overall, I would have to say that properly produced hemp oil from the right strains is very beneficial in the treatment of many mental disorders and is far safer to use than anything the medical system supplies.

Since 2013 when this book first came out there have been many new reports concerning the ability of these extracts to treat autism effectively. Many parents are now using these extracts to treat their autistic children and from the information I have received it appears that the use of this medication has proved to be of great benefit in the treatment of autism.

But more importantly I feel that we all need to understand why this condition has now become so prevalent in our society. From what I can understand it seems that the vaccines which have been forced upon our children, have a great deal to do with this dramatic increase in autism. So, I think that we as parents should all have the right to reject the use of vaccines even though in some countries their use has now become mandatory. If I wish to protect my children I would put my faith in these extracts to accomplish the task, rather than putting them at risk of acquiring autism from the effects of all these different vaccines.

GLAUCOMA, VISION

Glaucoma and its effects can be brought under control quite easily in most cases since many varieties of hemp are effective in dramatically reducing ocular pressure. It is not uncommon for a person suffering from glaucoma who is using hemp oil to see a substantial improvement in their vision. Many patients even have to get their glasses changed because their old prescription lenses are now too strong.

Do you think it makes sense that eye doctors will not even mention cannabis even though it has been known to be effective since at least the 1800s?
Again, extracts produced from the right strains is a very effective treatment for glaucoma and I know of nothing better or safer for reducing ocular pressure. The effect cannabis has on ocular pressure has been known for a very long time, yet the medical system tries to avoid even discussing hemp's use for glaucoma. Unfortunately, it appears that many doctors today are much more about money than they are about healing. I cannot explain how an eye doctor can sit there and watch a patient slowly go blind and not tell the patient what hemp can do for their condition. Far too often, in the end, patients lose their vision completely because they blindly trusted the advice of their doctors. Having a patient lose their ability to see correctly does not seem to mean much to many eye doctors. So, I think what they are doing is disgraceful and I feel very sorry for those who have been robbed of their vision for no reason other than greed.

HEART, BLOOD PRESSURE

Have you had any beneficial reports about hemp oil and heart conditions?

For those with heart problems who are commencing treatment with the oil, they should be aware that often this extract can increase a patient's heart rate, until they become comfortable with its use. The increase in heart rate is usually only slight, but I feel that the patient should know that it can happen.

This medication is effective to reduce cholesterol levels and improves blood circulation, so that in itself would be of great benefit to the patient's heart. Certainly, the heart is a vital organ and from our experience, hemp oil can rejuvenate vital organs. Although I have never told people to stop taking their heart medications, many have done so with no detrimental effects. I feel that hemp oil's effect on heart conditions requires more research, but from what we have seen, this medication appears to be very beneficial for the heart.

The original manuscript for this book was put out in 2013, but since that time new results have come in regarding the effectiveness of these extracts in treating heart problems. Around the end of 2014 my oldest friend suffered a heart attack, he had already used these extracts to save the life of his wife, so the night after his heart attack he began to ingest these extracts himself. Two months after he had suffered the heart attack, his heart showed no signs of damage at all and when tested by doctors it was proven that his heart was now operating at 157 above normal levels for a man of his age. So I think that these results should confirm the fact that there is nothing better to undo damage to the heart, than the use of these extracts.

Can the oil regulate blood pressure?

Hemp oil can regulate blood pressure, indeed. I use it myself to help me sleep and to regulate my own blood pressure. When commencing treatment with hemp oil, I tell patients who are already taking medication for this condition to keep a close eye on their blood pressure. Most who were using pharmaceuticals to control their blood pressure no longer require them upon commencing treatment with hemp oil.

Since hemp oil reduces blood pressure, anyone who tries to continue using their pharmaceutical blood pressure medications will likely find that the combination of the two will drive their blood pressure down too low. Although none as yet has really been harmed I still think that it's a good idea to avoid this situation and with the use of portable blood pressure monitors available today, this can easily be accomplished.

Can it help with other internal organ illnesses?

From what I have witnessed with the use of hemp oil, many internal organ conditions and associated problems can be controlled or cured. When an internal organ is rejuvenated and healed, it can once again resume its duties within our body. Personally, I think it makes much more sense to rejuvenate our own vital organs with the use of this oil, rather than to go through an organ transplant with all its associated dangers and then spending the rest of your life taking medications so the organ will not be rejected. In some cases, an organ transplant might be the only answer, but if this medication was used properly to rejuvenate vital organs, I believe that there would be much less need for transplants.

CHILDREN, SPORTSMEN, PREVENTION

Mothers in particular will worry if it is safe to give oil to children. Is it safe then?

I consider hemp oil to be perfectly safe in the treatment of children in all age groups who are suffering from cancer and other diseases. I really do not know how doctors treating small children in oncology units can live with themselves. Do they not know the damage they are doing to these little ones with their radiation, chemo, and other harmful, poisonous chemicals?

Anyone who has ever studied medicine knows the effects of such treatments and is aware of the fact that they are much more likely to produce harmful effects or even death with the use of these treatments, rather than a cure. If parents would only take the time to fully understand what the medical system intends to do to their children, I am sure that most would rather have them treated with hemp oil, because it is a natural substance that is safe to use and will cause no harm to the child.

Knowing what I do about the medical system, I would never let them get their hands on any child of mine. In the event that someone tried to force me to do otherwise, the situation would instantly turn very ugly indeed for I believe I have the right to protect their lives with any means at my disposal.

I think it is only natural that any parent would want to protect their children and keep them out of harm's way. If I thought the medical system presented a danger as the parent of the child, I would feel that I should have the right to choose other methods of treatment. Recently in the US and Canada, there have been cases where the authorities took children and forced them to take chemotherapy against both the wishes of the child and the parents themselves. It seems that as adults we have the right to reject their insane treatments, but our children do not. Since chemotherapy is simply poison, if anyone were to go against my will and administer such a thing to a child of mine, it could likely be said that they would not have a very bright future.

In my opinion, anyone who would do such a thing without the parents' consent is guilty of attempted murder and if the child were to die, they would then be responsible for their death. I don't care how you choose to look at it, poison is poison, and if a doctor administers these substances, they are just as guilty as I would be if I were to do the same. Just because doctors wear white coats does not mean they have the right to harm their patients; in fact, it goes against their own Hippocratic Oath. If I were them, I would start practicing medicine in the proper way before someone connected to the patients they have harmed decides to seek retribution against them.

How can hemp oil be used in disease prevention? Once again, would it also be safe to give the oil to children?

I know of nothing better than hemp oil to prevent diseases and I also consider this medication to be perfectly safe in the treatment of children. I have often stated that if children were given tiny doses of hemp oil, diseases like diabetes, MS, cancer, and many others could be prevented from ever occurring in most cases.

If minuscule doses of oil are given to children, THC and its associated cannabinoids will build up in their systems and prevent disease. I am not talking about getting children high; this is about providing children or people of any age with a harmless, non-addictive medicine to prevent medical problems in the future.

There is no logical reason why we should be prevented from growing and producing our own medicine to treat the ones we love. Should our children or even we ourselves be suffering and dying simply because drug companies wish to make more money? When there is a natural medication available to ease our medical problems that most people have little trouble producing? It's time to kiss the drug companies good bye and find out what Mother Nature can provide to keep ourselves and our children healthy.

How to dose hemp oil for children?

As for doses, children are no different than adults and they all have different tolerances for this medication. To prevent diseases in children, only miniscule doses would be required once a day about an hour before bedtime, so the chance of getting a child high would be very remote. Again, hemp oil does not cause any harm, so I do not know why anyone would hesitate in giving it to their children. In addition, imagine all the everyday injuries which take place that we could now treat ourselves if the oil was available. Things such as burns, cuts, scratches, sores, infections, insect bites, etc. can be treated so easily and effectively with the topical use of this oil.

After my experiences with this medication, it would be the first thing I would give my child for internal and external conditions. Yet, I definitely would hesitate and think twice before I would allow them to ingest chemical medications. In fact, knowing what I do about the medical industry, I would not even consider such a thing.

It takes experience with the healing effects of hemp oil to arrive at this way of thinking, but no doubt after seeing what it can do, you too will become converted. I firmly believe that if children and people of all ages were to take small doses of this oil on a regular basis, they could all live longer and be much more healthy.

Could hemp help athletes and sportsmen in any way?

Hemp would be very effective for athletes and sportsmen medicinally. Due to hemp's anti-inflammatory and rejuvenating properties and all its other wonderful healing effects, I can imagine nothing better for strained muscles or injuries than hemp oil.

Professional athletes are often given substances to numb the pain, but these medications do little to help heal the injury. In some cases, after taking such things, athletes will often try to play with the injury and this can cause further damage. When someone is injured, it takes time to heal, so I suggest to those who have suffered such things to take some time off and heal the injury properly with the use of this natural harmless medication.

Those who own teams that participate in professional sports may not like what I am saying. But they are not the ones who will have to suffer from all the damage that an athlete sustains during their careers. When an athlete reaches the stage when they can no longer compete in sports at this level, wouldn't it be better to see them walk off the field, rather than being carted away in an ambulance?

SYNTHETIC THC

There are manufacturers who produce synthetic THC and for some patients, it may have a positive effect on certain diseases. I do not doubt that there could be some truth to this, but why use something synthetic when the natural substance can be made so readily available?

There is only one reason drug companies produce synthetic THC and that is to make profit from patents while they deceive the public into believing that real research is being done. If helping the public was really their aim, they would have brought the healing power of this plant to the attention of the public years before its use was outlawed. Of course, why would they, since those who control these drug companies took part in having the hemp plant banned for medicinal use in the first place?

As far as I am concerned, the drug companies can keep their synthetic THC. From what I have gathered, synthetic THC is only effective in the treatment of about 13% of those who use the substance and it can come with undesirable side effects. Natural THC in hemp oil is by far superior to synthetic THC for the treatment of patients in most respects. The combination of all the different cannabinoid compounds in the resins of this plant work together to produce all these wonderful healing effects. So at present, I see no point other than greed for any company to produce synthetic THC in a laboratory.

DOCTORS, HIPPOCRATIC OATH

What do you think of the current medical system?

I have great respect for surgeons, or at least those who are good at what they do. Obviously, if you get in an accident or break a leg, we need somebody to put us back together. This side of medicine is more or less effective and is necessary if we are to recover properly.

Yet, when you look at the other side of the medical industry, with all of these doctors prescribing chemicals and poisons, as much as I hate to say it, from my perspective I consider them all to be little more than dealers in death. If doctors would simply follow their own Hippocratic Oath, they would not be administering these harmful substances and treatments to their patients. Instead, they would be using medications like hemp oil to heal those who come to them with medical issues.

A doctor's first obligation must be the well-being of those which they have under their care and they should not be concerned about the rewards that drug companies supply for pushing their products. The stated goal of medical professionals is to save lives and ease suffering and I think it's just about time that they started living up to the role they are supposed to be playing.

Have you ever treated a doctor?

In 2004, just after I had gone to the newspapers about this issue, I heard that Dr. David Rippey, a man who had been my family doctor in the past, was himself diagnosed with cancer. I had known Dave since the 1970's when he first came to Springhill to set up his practice. Since we had known each other so well, I contacted him and told him about this oil and what it could do to help his situation.

Dave confirmed that he did indeed have terminal cancer and he was scheduled to go to Ontario so they could try a new experimental chemo. He stated that if the chemo did not work, he would then be interested in giving this natural medication a try. Dave took the chemo and returned home but he never called me to provide the oil. A short time later, he passed away at the age of 55.

I also contacted another local doctor I knew well who was retired and explained to him what I had seen this medication heal. We talked for about two hours and he did show an interest, but after our conversation, I heard nothing more from him. For the most part, doctors in Canada tried to avoid me and the subject of hemp medicine if at all possible. But some patients suffering from cancer did tell me that their family doctors actually instructed them to get in touch with me for treatment.

Only one doctor in Canada has ever asked that I contact him directly and that was concerning a patient with terminal prostate cancer. This doctor told me that he would like to keep me informed as to the patient's progress during the treatment. Afterwards I never heard another word from him but three months later, the patient who was taking the oil called and told me that the doctor had stated he was cancer-free. One would think that doctors would be very excited about a cure for this dreaded disease, but this does not seem to actually be the case.

Countless Canadian doctors have seen patients with cancer and other conditions cured with the use of hemp oil but most say nothing. The problem with hemp medicine is that it exposes everything the medical system and our trusted doctors have been doing to the public. If you came to me and I gave you poison to treat your cancer, that would be attempted murder. If you took this poison and it killed you, I would then be guilty of murder. Yet, if a doctor gives you chemo or radiation and you die from the effects of it, that's called "medicine".

Any doctor with a lick of common sense knows the danger such treatments present to the public, but still they continue to provide them.

The vast majority of doctors in Canada today are more concerned about money and position than they are about healing their patients and doing their job properly.

Every time a doctor administers chemo or radiation etc., they are breaking their own Hippocratic Oath and they know it. I am not saying that good doctors do not exist but from my experience, it can only be said that they are very rare, especially in Canada.

A good number of doctors from foreign countries have contacted me about the use of this medicine. Some of these doctors themselves had cancer or they wished to produce the oil for a patient. Due to the so-called illegal nature of this medication, doctors who are using it tend to remain very quiet about what they are doing. Overall, I have received very little feedback from these doctors and only a few have contacted me back and informed me that the oil had worked.

I respect the work doctors like this are doing and I understand why they have to proceed quietly. As far as I am concerned, such doctors are helping me build an irrefutable database, which proves what this medicine can do. In the end, these doctors who are really trying to practice medicine properly will have much to do with bringing this medicine to the public, and for this, they have my deepest thanks.

In the Hippocratic Oath, doctors swear, "I will not give a lethal drug to anyone if I am asked." Do you think they observe that promise?
To me, the wording of the Hippocratic Oath is truly what medicine should be all about. Yet, with what I know about hemp oil and based on the response I have received from doctors thus far, I am afraid I must report that real doctors, who are in medicine to help their fellow man, are quite rare. It seems more than obvious to me that this oath they swear means nothing to the vast majority of them. These so-called medical professionals prescribe liver toxic poisonous chemicals, chemotherapy and radiation and they have the nerve to call what they are practicing "medicine."

To be truthful, these medical professionals have no excuse for what they are doing. They know the effects these treatments can cause, yet they continue to allow their patients to be subjected to such things. To make it clear to you just how bad things really are in the medical world, ask a ten-year-old child if they think poison and radiation are good for them. No doubt they will answer, "Of course not." Now ask your doctor the same question and they will tell you these so-called treatments are necessary if they are to treat you effectively.

It seems to me that someone has their wires crossed and, in reality, if a child knows more about medicine than those who work in this field, I think we are all in a great deal of trouble. To my way of thinking, doctors should have been the first to support the use of hemp medicine and any real doctor would never stand in the path of its use.

The way I look at it, doctors should have gone on strike over this issue years ago and demanded that this harmless medicine's use be allowed. According to all my experiences with the healing effects of hemp oil, trying to practice medicine without the use of cannabis really makes little sense. As a metaphor, it is like cooking without salt or trying to extinguish a fire without water.

When people are stricken with diseases like cancer, multiple sclerosis, AIDS, and many other serious conditions, they are afraid and do not know what to believe. The best thing anyone in this position can do is to educate themselves about their medical problems. Look into other forms of treatment that are available and decide for yourself what would be most beneficial to you. This is the kind of information your doctor should supply, yet unfortunately very few will discuss such matters. All doctors will talk about in most cases is what treatments the medical system provides. So if your doctor will not discuss alternatives, educate yourself, for your life could very well depend on your knowledge of such things.

People like to think that doctors have all the answers, yet if that were true, why are so many of us dying and suffering needlessly? As insane as it sounds, many with serious conditions who require this natural medication will have to break the so-called law if we want to survive. Laws are supposed to be put in place to keep our society operating in a safe manner and they must be based on the fact that what is being outlawed is causing harm. Yet sadly, when you look at the laws which were put in place against hemp's medicinal use, this is not the case. These laws were enacted so the public would have no choice other than to take the medical system's chemicals and poisons. So if you want to use hemp medicine to treat your condition, be prepared for the system to treat you like a criminal if you are caught. Their evil agenda will continue until we stand up for ourselves and tell them we are no longer willing to go along with their way of thinking.

A great many doctors will often tell you that you should not turn your back on the medical system and in some cases, I would agree. Still, if they are trying to convince you to take treatments which you know to be harmful and tell you it's a waste of time to try alternative therapies. I would tell them to keep their treatments or better yet take it themselves and I would be looking for a harmless alternative such as medicines that the hemp plant can provide.

Doctors are not telling those they treat to put their faith in the medical system out of concern for their patients, instead they make such statements to protect their profession and paychecks. For quite some time, the medical system has been much more about money than it is about healing. If this were not the case, why do they provide us with vastly overpriced chemicals and poison and call it medicine? Highly trained medical professionals know exactly what they are giving you. Their aim is to simply maintain the status quo and shove as many pills as possible into you, that is what is best for them, but not for those they are supposed to be treating.

TREATMENT OR MURDER?

Alan Levin, M.D. once wrote, "Most cancer patients in this country die of chemotherapy. Chemotherapy does not eliminate breast, colon, or lung cancers. This fact has been documented for over a decade. Yet, doctors still use chemotherapy for these tumors. Women with breast cancer are likely to die faster with chemo than without it." Don't you find it frustrating that this method is still used as the primary treatment for nearly all cancer patients?

With all the studies that have been done, exposing chemo and radiation for what they really are and all the harm such treatments cause to our bodies, I find it very hard to comprehend why anyone would prescribe or take poison and expect it to help a medical condition. Doctors who prescribe chemotherapy know exactly what they are giving their patients. What such doctors are doing is truly beyond belief, but more amazing still is the fact that patients so willingly do as their doctor tells them without weighing the consequences.

Chemotherapy is poison which will cause extensive damage to your body's vital organs and your immune system. In addition, the radiation our medical systems provide is no different. I often have wondered why they use the terms chemotherapy and radiation therapy, but I suppose few would take such treatments if they were called what they really are – poisontherapy.

Anyone that considers chemotherapy to be a viable medical treatment is either badly misinformed about its effects on our bodies or they are making such statements to protect their own twisted agendas. For the majority of those suffering from cancer, chemotherapy and radiation is just a faster way to die. Medical journals like The Lancet have produced studies with the same findings and I believe that they deserve some credit for their efforts. It is very refreshing to note that at least some of these medical publications are bringing out the real facts to protect us so why is it that doctors tend to ignore what their own medical journals state? When is the public going to awaken to what is being done to them by our medical systems and since when has injecting or ingesting a substance with a skull and crossbones on its packaging been considered to be good for you?

Did your mother ever tell you that chemicals, poison, and radiation are good for you? (Not likely.) So why do the public take such treatments from their doctors and unthinkingly do as they are told? When doctors start prescribing us all those chemicals and poisons, they have no idea what effect these so-called medications will have on us. We are all different, our tolerance for chemicals, poisons and many other substances vary from person to person. If you and I had the same type of cancer and took the same chemotherapy, the first dose may kill me. But if you happen to have a much higher tolerance for poison, you may escape the grim reaper for the time being.

Remember, every time you take chemo, you are poisoning every vital organ in your body. In the end, the vast majority of people are not saved by chemo, they die from its effects. Chemotherapy and radiation are both carcinogenic treatments. They do not cure cancer, they cause the condition and often help to spread it throughout the body. You can shrink a tumor with chemo and radiation but in the end, the effects of such treatments usually end up spreading the cancer.

Even medical journals like The Lancet tell us that chemo is just a faster way to die, but doctors continue to pass it out as if it were popcorn. It is not just chemo and radiation that the public should be wary of, but practically everything the medical system provides. Even things like CT scans, which doctors order every day, gives the patient a massive dose of radiation, which in turn can cause cancer or help to spread the disorder to other parts of the body.

A great number of medications that the medical system gives us are liver toxic. This means that such medications are poison to our livers. Do you actually think that poisoning your liver is going to help your medical problems and enable your body to heal in a faster way?

I strongly suggest that before taking any medications or treatments, the public should find out for themselves what such treatments could do to them. Look up the ingredients of the medications they are planning to put you on and decide for yourself if you really want to have these dangerous substances in your body. Just because doctors wear white coats does not always mean that they all know what they are doing or that they even care about what effect their treatments might have. It is your body and your life. Since the majority of doctors at present refuse to expose the truth, it is in the patient's best interests to find out for themselves.

Empiric medicine – medicine from plants – has been with us throughout history and hemp is the queen of all empiric healers. There has never been a recorded death due to the use of hemp medicine. It is too bad that what the medical system provides cannot make such claims themselves.

As I have stated, the safety of hemp medicine as a medication is unparalleled. If you were to ingest a large amount such a teaspoon of this oil or more, it will not kill you. An amount such as this would make you sleep for quite a long time, but when its effects wore off, you would be unharmed. Like any medication, there may be those who will not be able to use this substance for some reason. But I have never encountered anyone that suffered any major difficulties with its use, so as yet I still feel that it is beneficial for everyone. To me, overdosing on anything is fools' play in most cases and I warn the public to never try such things with pharmaceuticals, for you could end up in a coffin.

I do not recommend that anyone overdose on hemp oil unless they are in a life threatening medical situation. Still, if such a thing should accidentally happen or the patient's medical condition called for it, at least these extracts will do the patient no harm.

Don't you find it a bit absurd that many doctors would not take chemotherapy themselves, yet they administer it to patients?

The fact that many doctors will give their patients chemotherapy but would not take it themselves should highlight the lack of concern such doctors have for their patients. The public puts their trust in doctors to provide sound medical advice, which will help enable them to overcome their illnesses. But far too often they are simply misled by all the medical doubletalk and in the end allow themselves to be put in harm's way. Obviously, a great number of doctors feel their positions and paychecks are much more important to them than their patients' well-being, or they could not in good conscience be willing to prescribe such things as chemotherapy and radiation etc.

A few years ago, 72 oncologists attended a convention in Montreal and were asked if they themselves would take chemo or radiation if they were diagnosed with cancer. 59 out of the 72 cancer specialists in attendance said they would not take such treatments themselves. This means that only about 18% would even consider doing so, while 82% said they would not. If less than 20% of cancer specialists would take these treatments themselves, I think that this should tell us something. In time, this madness will end and soon most of us will be thinking about this issue in a more rational manner. But in the end the use of chemo and radiation plus other harmful substances must cease.

Obviously, doctors have to follow their code. Still, aren't they simply playing with their patients' lives?

Any codes that a doctor must follow should be based on the Hippocratic Oath and not on the profit margins of big drug companies. A real doctor's first obligation must be the welfare of their patients. If they refuse to follow their own oath, then such doctors are simply playing with their patients' lives, so they themselves and the drug companies can share in the profits. No matter how you look at it, what is currently taking place in reality could not be considered the practice of medicine by any rational thinking person. Instead, it could only be looked at as a very harmful and deadly con game, which the corruption of our governments has allowed those in control of drug companies to put in place.

What are the main advantages to this treatment when compared with chemotherapy, radiation or other chemical medications?

Hemp oil has three main advantages over so-called conventional treatments. First, hemp oil does no harm, second, it works, and third, it does not kill the patient. Chemotherapy, radiation and other poisonous chemical medications do extensive harm to the body and, in far too many cases, lessen our chance of survival. In addition, patients enduring such treatments often end up with other medical problems caused by these treatments themselves.

I cannot really compare hemp medicine to what the medical system provides, since I do not consider what they are giving us to even be medicine. Chemical medications are liver toxic. Which should make it obvious to anyone that such chemicals should not be in our bodies, since they are poison and present a danger to the patient.

Chemotherapy and radiation are both carcinogenic which means these treatments are not only poisonous, but they can also cause cancer as well. Often, the size of a tumor can be reduced with the use of chemotherapy or radiation but in a great number of cases, it simply allows the cancer to spread. Due to the carcinogenic effects of such treatments and their poisonous nature, they ruin your immune system when you need it most. In my opinion, it is ludicrous to call chemotherapy or radiation a treatment for cancer or any other condition, when obviously they should not be used at all.

Can using the oil replace radiotherapy?

The term radiotherapy sounds quite benign. It makes it seem as if all a patient has to do is listen to some music on the radio and they will get well. Of course as most of us already know this is far from what really takes place, so let's call it what it really is radiation therapy.

don't think radiation therapy is any better than chemotherapy, since of these treatments are poisonous and cancer-causing. Hemp medi-c... should be the first line of defense against cancer and all other illnesses, not treatments that could bring about our death or make our conditions worse.

As far as I can see, to allow the medical system to do such destructive things to our bodies is just a faster way to die. For some, chemotherapy and radiation does work as a delaying tactic, but in the end the damage these treatments do to your body is horrendous. If you are someone who happened to live through such treatments and their lasting effects, count your lucky stars because the vast majority are not so fortunate. In addition, I want to warn people that it's best to stay away from CT scans and such things, since they also expose patients to a massive dose of radiation which again can cause cancer or other health issues.

Hemp oil is not toxic to the body and when this oil is used to treat cancer or any other disease, it does not harm healthy cells. After taking hemp oil, it puts the patient in a very relaxed state so they can then get more rest and sleep, which promotes healing.

From my point of view, there is no comparison between chemical medications and hemp oil. Chemicals and poisons cause harm and affect your well-being; they can also have severe side effects and may even lead to death. Hemp oil is harmless and encourages good health and rapid healing. I like to say that this substance promotes life and from my experience with its use, I can actually report that this is the case.

Could hemp oil improve life expectancy?

If we all took small doses of hemp oil on a regular basis, I am firmly convinced we would all live longer and be much healthier. Longer life spans would be very beneficial to mankind, since it would allow those who have wonderful talents to accomplish so much more. Far too often in today's world, a person just gets good at what they are doing and they are then struck down with medical problems which end their careers.

We were all given this experience called life to broaden our abilities and horizons so our species can evolve to a higher level. In addition, nature has provided us with this wonderful plant to both preserve and protect our bodies from disease. It is impossible for me to comprehend that the human race could ignore this plant's healing potential any longer. Now that the truth about hemp's healing powers is available, we would be somewhat remiss in our duties to both ourselves and our loved ones if we did not demand this medicines free use immediately.

If you or anyone else on this earth would like to live longer in a state of excellent health to achieve the maximum potential of which we are capable, I do not see how anyone could feel they have the right to impose their will upon us or try to force anyone to abstain from the medicinal use of this plant. Since life is supposed to be about living and now you have found a way to avoid all this needless suffering, I wish you all a very long and healthy existence.

You must have heard so many people telling you, "This can't work, nothing will help, the doctor said I will suffer from this for the rest of my life..."

A great number of patients have come to me with medical conditions their doctors had no success in treating and they felt their situation was hopeless. Quite often, people do not even have a diagnosis as to what is really wrong with them because in reality doctors could not provide them with an answer. Most of these patients that I provided oil to did not believe hemp could help their conditions until they tried the treatment. I have been in contact with thousands of individuals, who were completely astounded by what this medication did for their conditions. If hemp oil is unable to cure your condition, you will more than likely find that these extracts are by far the best control available.

Doctors like to tell us that many diseases and conditions are incurable, but this medication pays little attention to the opinions of doctors and often works what are considered to be medical miracles. If you have a medical problem, give the oil a try and there's a good chance you will see the miracles it can produce for yourself.

Does it make sense to not provide people with hemp-based medicines?

It makes absolutely no sense to prohibit hemp's medicinal use to the public and in reality, no one has the right to do such a thing. The only reason that hemp was ever prohibited in the first place was due to the fact that it presented a real danger to many big money concerns. Restricting the medicinal use of the most medicinal plant on earth to those who inhabit this planet could only be termed as being a crime against humanity. It seems at present governments are still willing to let their rich friends who own the drug companies have their way, but in the end they will be unable to hold the truth about the effectiveness of this medication back.

When cannabis hemp makes its return to mainstream medicine, it will destroy all the corruption that ever stood against its free medicinal use. This plant is quickly becoming recognized once more as being the greatest healing plant in existence and medications produced from it will change the face of medicine forever. Soon the public will reject the chemicals and poisons we currently call medications and they will demand the use of this natural substance, so they can heal themselves sensibly.

Isn't the oil a giant leap forward in the field of medicine?

Hemp oil is more than a giant leap forward in the treatment of diseases, because we now have the means to heal medical conditions without doing the patient harm. In reality, this is the way that medicine should have always been practiced, but greed has taken our society down the wrong path when it comes to healing and many other things. In the treatment of cancer and other life-threatening conditions, this natural oil can be used harmlessly to treat the disease and it can also be used to prevent the illness from ever occurring. In addition, this substance can often cure conditions which were thought to be incurable, so vast numbers of those who are currently suffering now have a chance to recover. Smoking hemp does have limited medicinal value and controlling nausea is definitely one of them. Still, isn't it a bit insane to watch someone smoke cannabis to prevent the nausea caused from chemo when the very same plant material, if properly processed and taken, could possibly cure their cancer?

The medicinal wonders of this plant have always been right before us and it is a great shame that it has taken so long to find the proper way in which it can be used to heal our medical problems. Countless individuals have suffered and died needlessly due to the lack of proper treatment, but now that we know the medical wonders this plant can produce, the human race should soon see an end to their suffering.

THE POLICE COMES IN

You gave away oil from hundreds of kilos of hemp. How did you feel when the police came?

In 2003, I was raided by the RCMP and they confiscated well over a hundred and fifty plants, but I was never charged in connection with this raid.

Then in 2005, I put another 1620 hemp plants in my back yard, which caused the RCMP to stage another raid, but this time charges were laid. In addition, in 2006 I had another 1100 clones from strong medicinal varieties of cannabis which were again confiscated from my property by the RCMP. Believe me the whole experience was very disturbing when I realized how deep the corruption ran and I feel these crops were simply stolen by the police at the government's request.

I consider what the RCMP did in my case to be a crime because they knew the hemp I was growing was used to produce medicine and I had made no secret of my activities. Since so many in the surrounding area had used this substance I was producing to deal with many different medical issues, it was obvious that the medication I manufactured was helping vast numbers. If indeed it were true that the RCMP are not corrupted, why would they so willingly try to put a stop to the production of this medicine? There was no shortage of evidence to prove what this substance could do and that it was helping so many of the people who are paying their salaries?

On May 6, 2005, three months before I was charged, I even provided the RCMP with videotaped evidence, showing patients who had used the oil for their medical conditions. In the information I provided with this video, I also asked that the RCMP provide me with the hemp they confiscated so I could produce more medication for the public. On this same video, I informed them that I was growing hemp right in my back yard and how I planned to put it to good medicinal use. Three months later, on August 3, 2005 the same RCMP detachment which I had provided the evidence to raided my property and pretended to know nothing of the video and information I had given them.

What I witnessed during these different raids was police work right out of the *Twilight Zone* or some other upside down form of reality. But of course these brave officers were just doing their jobs or at least that was the excuse they tried to use to convince themselves that they were actually doing nothing wrong. I think a standard requirement for individuals who wish to join any police force would be the ability to know right from wrong. The police officers I encountered showed no remorse whatsoever for their actions and that is why I feel officers of this caliber should not be allowed to police any society.

Obviously these were very sick-minded individuals who apparently have mental issues which gives them this brain dead attitude. But I think those who are given the right to wear badges and guns to keep law and order should be a bit more rational and realize the responsibility they have to the public. Or else they simply present a danger to those they are supposed to serve and since people actually died due to the raids they performed on my property this should not be tolerated.

As far as I am concerned, the RCMP are a total fraud and in my opinion this organization should be disbanded, due to the harm they have caused. The RCMP are supposed to be working for the public's best interests and not the profit margins of big drug companies. I must say that the raids conducted by the RCMP on my property have left me very disillusioned with the country of my birth. It seems that one must be very wary of any organization that has a name which starts with "Royal Canadian" since in many cases you will find such organizations are government controlled and do not work for the public.

I am not saying that Canada does not need a national police force, but I do think the Canadian people deserve a police force which they can take pride in and trust. The RCMP have shamed themselves by working against the greater good of the Canadian people who pay their wages. So to me, the only rational thing to do would be for the RCMP to step aside and allow a police force with integrity to take their place.

Did they return the plants?

I have been raided four times by the RCMP and they have never given anything they confiscated from my home or property back. Even after the three raids that resulted in no charges being laid had taken place, they always kept whatever was confiscated. To me, what they are doing is nothing more than legalized theft and obviously, if no charges were laid, whatever they had taken should at least be returned. It was not just hemp plants that the RCMP removed from my property, during their raids other articles unrelated to growing hemp were also taken. From my perspective, they just seemed to confiscate whatever caught their eye and there did not appear to be any rhyme or reason to what they were doing.

If you or I took something from someone's property, after being caught and charged we would be expected to return what was taken. But if the RCMP removes something from your property even if it is unrelated to any crime, you will probably never see it again. Could behavior like this from our national police force really be described as upholding the law, when it is obvious they are committing crimes against the citizens of this nation? Or are they simply nothing more than a pack of thieves and bullies who are being highly overpaid to do the government's dirty work?

The court proceedings must have left you with very unpleasant feelings. You were helping people for free, many of them got up from their deathbed and you still had to go through the trial.

By early 2008, when my court case finally came to an end, I was so fed up with all the corruption I had witnessed that I was ready to leave Canada. Of course, by this time I had come to know better than to expect honesty or compassion from the Canadian legal system or the government that controls them, since it appears that in both legal and government circles they have no understanding or interest in the concept of justice at all. Half the lawyers in Canada are making a good part of their living defending or prosecuting people facing hemp charges. Once all these lawyers get lined up at the money truth, justice and human rights mean nothing.

Everyone present during my court case knew I was speaking the truth about the wonders of this medicine, but it was ignored in favor of corruption and greed. The Canadian legal system is guilty of helping the government perpetrate this crime against the Canadian people and my case proves that this is indeed a fact. I would tell anyone seeking justice that they will not find it in the legal system or courtrooms of my homeland.

What kind of country is Canada when they will drag a person such as myself through their corrupted legal system, then break every rule in the book to see that you are convicted and made to look like a criminal for the simple act of helping others? The hemp oil I produced eased suffering and saved many lives and in addition when I had the medication available, I gave it to patients free of charge. If such behavior is a crime in Canada, maybe it's time for a few changes. In the end, hemp medicine will destroy all the corruption which stands against its use, and when that day comes, we will all be able to see who the real criminals are.

At the end of my court case, my followers and I were firmly convinced I had won the case hands down. The prosecution it seems were also aware of this and stooped to jury tampering to see that I was convicted. A lady who had been present when my verdict came in called me the very next day and informed me that this was what had transpired.

I had treated relatives of some of those who had sat on my jury, so I could not imagine that they would convict me of anything. I was completely shocked when they pronounced me guilty of all three charges I had been facing, all I could think was, "Guilty of what? Healing?" Then, when the lady had called and explained what she had witnessed, it all made sense. Would the crown tamper with the jury to see that I was found guilty so it would send the message that I was a criminal and that this medication didn't really work? To me it appeared that this is what had actually transpired.

During my court case, they would not even give those who had used the oil to treat their conditions the opportunity to testify. So it was not hard for me to believe that they may have tampered with the jury also. The judge was made aware that a witness had seen the crown prosecutor leaving the jury room about three minutes before the jury came in with their verdict.

About two weeks later we were called back to the courthouse and the judge threatened the lady who had witnessed the event with 14 years in prison for perjury if they found anything she said on the stand to be untrue. She took the stand and they could not disprove anything she was saying and after questioning her extensively, she was dismissed. Since what she had stated had not been disproved in any way and the judge did not send her to jail for perjury as he had threatened, one would think that at the very least my case should have been dismissed because after this lady's testimony had been given, obviously the verdict that had been passed down to me was now in question.

I may not know much about their brand of justice, but from my perspective what took place that day almost defies description. The jury was not even called in to testify and the RCMP did not do an investigation, so it appears that if the crown prosecutor has been accused of a crime such things are not necessary. Then to top it all off, the judge stated that he thought this was just something that this lady and I had cooked up to derail my sentencing. If that were really the case, why was he not sending her to jail as he had threatened?

In the past, I have heard the expression kangaroo court, but now I was standing in one. If anyone can look at proceedings like this and call them just, I would have to say that they likely belong in a mental institution. Jury tampering is a very serious charge unless you happen to be the crown prosecutor, in which case the judge simply sweeps it all under the rug. This is what passes for justice in Canada and so it shall remain, until it is replaced by a legal system that really does have the best interests of the public at heart.

What was the sentence and what implications does it have for you?
At my sentencing, I was facing 12 years in prison but it seems the judge must have had an attack of conscience before I was sentenced. During my sentencing, he stated that under different circumstances, I would be given awards and honors for my work but that is not why I was brought into this court. He then went on to say that in his 34 years in the legal system he had never seen a case like this; there was no criminal intent. After making this statement, he then admitted that the scientific evidence does exist to back up everything I was saying. The judge also stated there were many people who had used the oil for their medical conditions and they too backed my position.

From my perspective, what the judge said at my sentencing did not even make any sense because he had never heard any evidence during my case to back up the statements he was making. When my case was taking place, the judge would not allow the patients to testify, so he had heard no testimony from them whatsoever. In addition, he kept me from introducing the scientific evidence I had gathered, so how would he have knowledge of their existence, since he would not allow them to be introduced into evidence? Obviously, this judge must have had prior knowledge that everything I was telling the court was true, because he had allowed no testimony to that effect during my trial.

So why had he not allowed the patients to testify and what purpose was served by refusing to let the scientific evidence be introduced during my trial? It seems very strange to me that a Supreme Court Judge would make comments like this after bending over backwards to see that I was convicted.

In addition, since the judge admitted everything I had stated was true, why were they not crying out for joy that the medicine of our dreams had been found? Instead, the sentencing went on as if nothing had happened and people continued to die because the legal system refused to deal with this case properly.

I was given a $2,000 fine and a gun restriction. I believe I was given the fine because I spoke out very loudly about what they were doing during my court case. As for the gun restriction, it's simply nonsense since there were no firearms found during the RCMP raids anyway. The only ones waving guns around were the police themselves. It seems, for some obscure reason, a gun restriction is put in place for ten years if you are convicted of trafficking even if you don't own a gun and if you have been convicted more than once, the restriction is lifelong. I was tied up in our legal system for three long years and in the end, this was the result. I was not even put on probation, so it appears their aim was to simply discredit me and my work.

After going through the greatest kangaroo court case in Canadian history, I can only say that we live in a beautiful country but it is corrupted to the core. My father fought in Normandy and was badly wounded fighting for this country and what he perceived to be freedom. Now Canada has turned into the very thing my father was fighting against in WWII and in many ways, it is even worse. After what I have seen those in authority do I am no longer proud to call myself a Canadian, in fact, the country of my birth means practically nothing to me now.

My own nation and most others worldwide are simply allowing their citizens to be slaughtered so big money interests can keep up their profit margins. This combined with the fact that Canada along with the U.S. and other countries are invading foreign nations simply over greed and resources, leaves me with the impression that Canadians and others who live in countries which are committing these crimes have very little to be proud of. I can honestly say that due to what I have seen our leaders do, I will never look at Canada the same again. Now I truly feel like a man without a country because my own homeland has proven to be such a disappointment but somewhere on this planet I hope that one day I will find for a country that is much less corrupted that I can dwell in.

It may not seem like much, but on behalf of the Canadian people, I wish to apologize to the countries which have been harmed due to the actions of our government and the troops they sent there. Most Canadians are good people but unfortunately, our country is being run by rogues and villains who want to steal the resources of foreign lands. Finally, other nations are starting to recognize the horror in what countries like the US and Canada are doing, but as yet, the so-called free world is still beating the drums of war.

The change is coming and I hope one day to see the end of all wars and when that day arrives, we may finally learn to live in peace. In the meantime, we must keep striving to build something better to bring this about and when we succeed, the rewards will be well worth the effort. Good health and a better way of life is something we all desire and with the free use of the hemp plant plus a little common sense that goal is now achievable.

Do you think people in law enforcement do not realize that sooner or later they might need this medication for themselves?

Many people in law enforcement definitely know that hemp medicine works and they should all realize that they have no right to interfere with its medicinal use. As a matter of fact, I have supplied this medication to a good number of those who are employed in our legal system and policing. RCMP officers have even sent patients to me for treatment, who were dying of terminal cancer, so many officers are aware that this natural substance works. The police are no different than we are when it comes to disease, they too are afraid of cancer and other serious conditions.

Yet the police seem to have a very hard time getting their heads around the fact that our government's policies towards hemp medicine is killing them and their families as well. Most police officers try to brush off their wrongdoing in regards to the raids they perform against those who use hemp medicine by saying that they are just doing their jobs. But that is the same excuse those who worked in Hitler's death camps used and it did not justify their behavior then, nor does it justify the behavior of police forces today.

It's time the police woke up to the reality of what they are doing. Do police officers actually believe that it's wrong for the public to grow the most medicinal plant on earth to produce this medication? Or would they themselves not be looking for these extracts if they had a loved one who was dying and needed treatment? I expect that they would, so maybe it's time for the police to start pointing their guns at the real criminals.

To deny hemp medicine's use to the public is a crime and the police must stop enforcing laws which were put in place against hemp's use for medicinal purposes. Cannabis hemp is simply a natural harmless healing plant. So how could the police or anyone else think they have the right to deprive someone with a serious medical problem from being allowed the free use of this substance?

Do you think you will ever stop producing the oil?

Under Canadian law, there is no provision for anyone to produce hemp oil for medicinal use or to gather the resins from the hemp plant. I spent years ingesting medications from doctors that did more harm than good for my condition. The only medication that has ever helped my situation was cannabis hemp and the oil it can produce. Even though I asked dozens of doctors for a prescription so I might use this substance legally, I was refused. From my position, I had no choice other than to produce the medicine myself and I plan to continue doing this until the day I die.

The legal system could come and put me in jail and deny me the use of this medicine, but if they do, then their actions could kill me. If the medical system actually had a medication that would help my condition, they may have a leg to stand on, but they do not. So, if I end up in jail with no medicine and this causes my death, the public will know how our corrupted system brought this about.

I don't take this substance for no good reason, I need it to survive and if I die fighting for the right of us all to use this substance, at least my death will not have been in vain. Soon, mankind will have free access to this amazing medicine and no amount of corruption can stop this from transpiring, when that day comes, the face of medicine will change forever.

How do you feel when you have to deny someone treatment simply because you don't have enough hemp to make the medicine?

I have people coming to me all the time who cannot afford the prices charged for cannabis by drug dealers and most other growers. I do the very best I possibly can for everyone but unfortunately my finances are not a bottomless pit.

I have now spent what savings I had trying to supply those who were in need of this medication and I simply do not have the funding to carry on in this manner. I feel a great deal of frustration, due to the fact that if hemp were grown freely, a pound of high-grade medicinal hemp would be worth little more than a pound of corn.

It seems inconceivable that people are dying simply because they cannot afford the starting material needed to make this natural medicine. Until this situation is rectified and we can freely produce this medication, I encourage everyone to grow their own. Current government policies restricting hemp's medicinal use will soon disappear, but in the meantime, self-supply is the name of the game.

If you have a loved one that is suffering or dying that needs this medication, who gives a damn about absurd laws and government policies? As a human being, you have a right to this medicine's use no matter what any corrupt government policies or laws have to say.

Remember, laws are just paper and ink and if corruption was used to put them in place as they were in regards to hemp, you are not committing any real crime by producing this medication. So if you or someone who is close to you has a life threatening condition isn't it about time to throw the rule book out the window and do something rational for a change? Many years ago, I was forced to do just that if I wanted to live and for doing this I have no regrets, so until this world starts making some sense I would urge you to do the same.

RESEARCH

The system will have a hard time swallowing this. Anyway, a change is necessary and medical marijuana seems to be a necessity...

There is no doubt hemp will soon once again take its rightful place in mainstream medicinal use and will be widely used everywhere as it was for thousands of years in the past. No matter if the medical system likes to hear it or not, their allopathic approach of treating those with medical problems using chemicals and poisons does not work. Empiric medicine (medicine from plants) is our only viable safe alternative. After thousands of years of medicinal use, the hemp plant and many other herbs have shown us their value in the field of medicine and we would have to be insane to ignore their use any longer.

Currently, the population of this planet is in the middle of a cancer epidemic and also many other diseases seem to be out of control as well. At no time in man's history have we ever needed a medicine so badly, which can relieve the suffering of such vast numbers. Since hemp oil can treat cancer of all types in a sensible and safe manner and is also so effective in the treatment of other conditions, what better time to reintroduce hemp's medicinal use?

For far too long we have been told nothing but lies about this plant by our governments and those who control them. They tell us things like cannabis hemp is a gateway drug, which will cause those who use it to go on and become addicted to the use of hard drugs. This is nothing but a pack of lies and in reality hemp oil is very effective in helping people break their addictions to these dangerous substances. How could a natural medication that helps to break addictions cause people to seek out and ingest hard drugs and pharmaceuticals, to which they can become addicted?

To me, statements which refer to cannabis as being a gateway drug are only used to keep the public misinformed. If indeed hemp is a gateway, it is a gateway back for those with addictions and vast numbers who are suffering with other serious conditions. I think that it's about time that governments started giving their citizens the real truth about this plant. If not, then I expect that they will have a dim future once the public finally learns the truth. Word of what this medicine can do is spreading rapidly and now the medicinal use of the hemp plant will be held back no longer.

When every second person knows how to cure their own cancer with hemp, how can the corruption of our system stand against its use? In the near future those who populate this planet will have access to the medicine they require and I would not want to play the role of anyone who tried to get in the way. The public will only take so much and if nothing positive is done quickly, I would not want to be on the receiving end when the people lash out. So as you can see, what happens next depends upon the way those who have been pretending to represent us react. We can either do this the easy way or we can do it the hard way, so if those who are currently in charge choose to be difficult, I'm sure they will regret their actions in a very short time.

What should research focus on?
In the near future, the most important thing to do is grow the best medicinal strains possible, so we can determine their true medical virtues. Since this medication is harmless, we can do whatever research is required while we are healing the people.

Some strains of cannabis are much more effective than others in treating different medical situations. In a short time, we should be able to determine the best strains to treat any given condition and this will allow these disorders to be treated more effectively. In addition, we must put some form of quality control in place as quickly as possible and develop standards that suppliers must adhere to. At present, patients have no idea about the quality or effectiveness of oils, which they are purchasing from others. Truly, much research is yet to be done on this plant's medicinal qualities, but if we go about it in the proper way, in a short time I think that we can learn a great deal.

In March 2011, we witnessed the nuclear power plant disaster in Japan, within this book you will find an article I wrote concerning the danger this presents to us all. If you take the time to go over it, I think you will be relieved to know that this medication can help protect us from the radiation damage that is emanating from Japan, and this is just one more reason this substance must be made available as quickly as possible.

I hope to live to see the day when everyone on earth has access to hemp medicine that is made available to them on a donation basis. No one should have to suffer because they cannot afford the medicine that could heal them and since hemp medications can be produced so cheaply, I cannot see any reason why this would not work.

Written in July 2009, edited in June 2013 and September 2016.

CHAPTER 4

HEMP: THE CURE-ALL WITH A THOUSAND MEDICINAL PROFILES

I am providing this information so people may have a better understanding of the medicinal values of hemp and why the system is so afraid of a plant. It seems that practically all hemp has medicinal virtues, but the medicinal values from strain to strain can vary a great deal. Hemp is the most misunderstood of all healing herbs and it also happens to be the most harmless and effective healing plant on earth.

Before I go into all this, I will try to explain as simply as possible why governments and those in control have kept the truth about this plant hidden. Throughout history, many lies and deceptions were employed by those in powerful positions to keep the public at large ignorant in regards to hemp's true medicinal values. Even religion played a disturbing role in keeping the truth about this plant withheld from the public.

For the most part, this was done to keep the human race enslaved and under their control. People who use hemp tend to question what is going on and quite often will not go along with the rest of the herd. For a very long time, this has been duly noted by those who are trying to maintain control. So for many of those in authority throughout the ages, keeping the truth about the healing power of this plant from the public was a necessity if they were to remain in charge.

Indeed, if the public knew the truth, then practically everyone would be using this plant properly as a medication to maintain good health. A situation like this would cause many more people to start questioning the policies of the so-called powers that be and that, my friends, is what they are so afraid of.

Do you think that big money concerns would like to deal with a public who now know the truth and are thinking much more rationally? A public that will no longer swallow the lies and deceptions and a public that will now put a stop to their policies and projects that are harming the human race and this planet?

It's a classic battle between good and evil. If we don't put a stop to the agenda of these people who are now running things, the human race may soon become extinct due to the damage we are allowing them to do to us and this earth. Therefore, there is only one rational thing to do – legalize hemp's use as medicine and put mankind back on a course that makes some sense.

From the past performance of those who are currently in charge, it is abundantly clear that they have not been working for the greater good of the people. Obviously, what has been motivating them is the pursuit of money and power and all this has been done at the expense of the public's health and well-being. In the future, this type of behavior can no longer be tolerated from those who are put in positions of public trust.

The goal of anyone employed in such positions must be to do the job properly and always work for the greater good of the people. Everything must be done with an open book policy to the public and nothing should be hidden. In addition, their work must be scrutinized by an honest news media, whose only aim is to see that the public gets the truth. It's not hard to change the world in which we live; all that is required is the will to make it happen.

What people often fail to understand about the hemp plant is the great diversity of medicinal uses from strain to strain. Some strains are more effective as a painkiller, while other varieties may be better for a diabetic to control their blood sugar levels or someone who is trying to lower their ocular pressure that suffers with glaucoma.

Luckily, it seems that for the most part high quality medicinal cannabis indica strains are an effective treatment for all types of cancer. There are now thousands of different types of cannabis that have come into being due to breeders crossing different strains. The three main varieties of this plant are cannabis indica, cannabis sativa and cannabis ruderalis. Pure indicas produce a very sedative medication that is effective in the treatment of most medical conditions.

Good indica strains that have been crossed with sativa or ruderalis can also possess this heavy sedative medicinal effect. Yet, it depends a great deal on the percentage of indica that is present in these new crosses as to how effective they will be as a medication. Generally, the higher the indica content, the more sedative and effective these crosses will be as a medicine.

Pure sativa, on the other hand, produces an energetic effect, which is not conducive to promote healing in most cases and can interfere with the sleeping patterns of those who try to use it as a medication. Medications produced from pure sativa or sativa dominant indica or ruderalis crosses can be beneficial in the treatment of someone suffering from depression, or skin conditions that can be treated topically.

For ingestion purposes, oils produced from sativa and sativa dominant crosses must be used with caution. Such oils can be unbelievably energizing when ingested and this effect, in my opinion, does not promote the healing process.

In the last few years, cannabis ruderalis has gained a lot of attention in the hemp world. As I understand it, ruderalis is being crossed with indicas and sativas to make these strains more hardy and mold resistant. In addition, ruderalis varieties can be high in CBD content and some think this could be of great importance, but it is yet to be proven. I cannot voice an opinion as to how effective medications produced from this variety would be medicinally. Since I have no experience working with ruderalis varieties, at this time I do not feel qualified to offer my opinions.

Still, for best results, I would use pure indica or indica dominant sativa crosses to produce this medication, because they have already been proven to be effective.

For someone new to the world of hemp, all this can be quite bewildering. Due to all the breeding that has been done, the old way of just looking at the large leaves on the plant to determine if it is an indica or sativa can no longer be trusted. Traditionally, the large leaves on sativa strains were long and thin, while the large leaves of indicas were much broader in appearance due to all the cross breeding which has been done. Now a plant can look like an indica, yet exhibit the energizing traits of a sativa and vice versa. All this can be very hard for a beginner to comprehend, so I would suggest that people approach this problem in the same way I did.

The easiest way to determine what traits bud material has within it is to simply smoke some and see what effect it has on you. When people bring hemp to me to produce this medication, I roll a joint. By the time I have smoked about half of it, I know if it possesses the sedative effect I am looking for and that is how I select the material I use.

If you are going to buy hemp to produce medication and do not smoke it yourself, take someone along who is an experienced smoker and have them try some of the material you are thinking of purchasing. Tell them that you are looking for a strong sedative effect and you do not want to buy something that is uplifting or energizing.

It's also not a bad idea to bring a pocket magnifier along, so you can examine the resin on the bud you intend to purchase. Good bud looks like it is covered in frost, most of the time it can even be seen with the naked eye. Once you get used to producing the oil, one can often get a pretty good idea how much oil a strain may produce per pound just by looking at the bud material with a magnifier. The resin you are observing is the medicine and generally speaking the more that is present on the bud material, the larger the amount of oil it will produce.

From my experience, practically all highly dominant indica strains can produce a medication that is an effective treatment for many medical conditions. Even people suffering from depression can benefit from the effects of oils produced from good indicas. So it's best to stay away from sativas to produce medicine for most internal purposes. Still, if you wish to treat a skin condition or skin cancer topically, I think you will find that oils produced from sativa varieties can be quite effective in the treatment of such things. There is no question that some strains produce a much more potent medication than others for different medical conditions. In the future, that is where the research must be done.

We already know the miracles this medication is capable of. Now all we have to find out is which strains are the most beneficial to treat different conditions. This can all be accomplished using a simple process of elimination and the research can be done while we are healing the people. I hope my explanations in this article have been helpful to the many people in need of this medication.

CHAPTER 5

ONWARD TO FULL LEGALIZATION

Just a couple of days before Jack Herer collapsed with a heart attack, he informed Steve Hager that if anything happened to him, the torch was to be passed to me. Upon Jack's death, Steve made his wishes known publicly at his graveside service, so from that time on I have more or less become the leader of the hemp movement in Jack's place.

I really did not expect this and would have been perfectly happy to continue with my work on the medicinal front of the movement. Yet, it seemed Jack apparently thought I was capable of much more, so if there are no objections, let us move onward to complete legalization.

To me, Jack Herer was one of the greatest natural rights activists that ever lived. The knowledge he gave us and the words he spoke were not for the benefit of one particular group, they were for the benefit and greater good of all mankind. Jack was my friend and mentor, he spoke from the heart, and he was one of a kind. He had seen the direction my actions were taking the hemp movement and Jack was 100% behind me.

Only a fool would be capable of thinking that they can just step in and fill the shoes of a man such as Jack Herer. Still, it seems that this is the task that Jack has left to me and I will do my best to honor his wishes and memory. I may now be the leader of the hemp movement, but we have only ever had one Emperor and his name is Jack Herer. So, long live his memory and the dream he had for us all.

The system has always labeled people like Jack and I as being radicals. The fact is there is nothing radical about us as far as hemp or anything else is concerned, we were simply speaking the truth. The reason the system calls us radicals is simply because the truth we are speaking exposes their corruption. So they use all their money and power to try to discredit us to the public – for this is the only way they can maintain control.

Jack like myself felt that no one has the right to deny anyone the medicinal use of this harmless plant. In truth, the hemp plant should be playing a vital role in detoxifying this earth, providing medicine, energy and a vast array of other products that would be of a great benefit to mankind.

To witness people like Eddy Lepp being imprisoned for growing this wonder of nature is intolerable. What has the world come to when a man such as Eddy is locked up for ten years because he committed the crime of helping his fellow man?

The injustice that has been committed against so many innocent people defies all description and must come to an end. The will of big money must no longer overrule the will of the people. My aim is to see that hemp becomes completely legal once more for anyone to grow and possess free of taxation. It would be utter insanity for us to willingly pay tax to the very system that has kept this plant's use from us and which in turn has harmed so many of our friends and family members.

Rise as one and let the system know that we are aware of what they have been doing to us. Inform them that we are no longer willing to line up like farm animals and take their poisons and chemicals as medicine.

What is needed right now is a peaceful resolution to the situation we are in. Why can big money interests not work with us to achieve a smooth transition that will benefit all mankind? How much money do these people really require and by what right did they ever think only they are fit to control the masses so they can maximize their profits?

In the world we live in at the present time, money is power but when it is used against the greater good of mankind, it is definitely time for a change. I will not rest until the day comes when a police officer looks at a field of hemp no differently than a field of corn.

We must dispel all the lies and deceptions the system has fed the public about the cannabis hemp plant. This is the only way we can possibly put the human race back on the right track. Grow hemp everywhere. Not only for medicine, but for food, fuel, fiber, textiles … the list is endless. Put the people back on the land where they belong so they can once again get in touch with what's important – their own self sufficiency, mother nature, and the well-being of this planet.

You might say I have looked at the hemp movement from the inside out. On the surface, we look united but in reality we are very fragmented.

There are people in the movement like Marc Emery from Canada who made statements in his interview for the book *Bud Inc.* that sounded as if he were not in favor of hemp's complete re-legalization. Unless I misunderstood what was in the book or don't remember it correctly, I cannot imagine how anyone that would make such a statement could consider themselves to be an activist. We have allowed people like this to play important roles in the movement, when in reality they have hidden agendas.

As far as I am concerned, if you are not for the full repeal of these absurd laws, you are not in the movement. For decades, our own apathy has allowed the system to lead us around by the nose as if we had no right to question their policies. To make matters even worse, we even went along with them when we all knew what they were doing was wrong. So in reality we are all to blame for what has happened in the past, but that does not mean we should allow it to continue.

Today I hear many people shouting, "Legalize all drugs," but the thought of this scares me. Due to the self-destructive nature of the human race, a policy such as this could have many serious repercussions. I do not want my children exposed to things that can harm them. I would also not want them to have free access to such substances to experiment with. Like many others, I have seen the destructive nature of poisons and chemicals supplied by drug companies and what they do to people who use them.

As I understand it, over 80% of deaths from drug abuse are related to the use of such drugs. Other street drugs like alcohol, crack, and crystal meth etc. also take their toll but pharmaceuticals are by far the greatest danger.

If hemp were used properly, it could put an end to the use of all these dangerous substances. Why take something to heal yourself or for relaxation that is dangerous to your health, when hemp can provide the same effect harmlessly?

Extracts from the hemp plant can also be used to make it much easier for those who are addicted to dangerous substances to withdraw from their use. The system tells us that marijuana has a gateway effect, which will cause those who use it to throw away their lives and become addicted to hard drugs. Statements like this are utter nonsense. How can a medication which is useful in breaking addictions cause someone to become addicted to the same dangerous substances which cause this problem?

I would agree that hemp oil is a gateway drug, but it is a gateway back for people suffering with addictions and it does not take those who use it down the road to destruction, as our governments would have us believe. Once you really get to know what medications produced from this plant can do, you will find that its medicinal uses are limitless.

Of course, there will still be many standing there in their white coats, saying that this plant's medicinal use still requires more research before it is safe for the public to consume or that it must be controlled and taxed. They are uttering such statements either due to complete ignorance of the subject at hand or to protect their own positions. Politicians, lawyers, and police officers etc. will often voice this same nonsense and they are simply doing this to protect their positions and justify their actions.

This shows how much they actually care about the well-being of the public who are paying their salaries. These individuals have all been living a lie but now it's time for sober thinking. I am openly challenging the system to come and defrock what I have been telling the public about the healing power of the hemp plant.

From where I am standing, it would take a fool to openly stand against the free use of hemp in medicine. Unbelievably, people who are against hemp's medicinal use have loved ones of their own who are suffering that this medicine could heal. What kind of thinking is required for them to behave in this manner and how much longer do they actually expect to get away with it?

The healing qualities of this plant have been known for a very long time. It seems almost unbelievable that the so-called powers that be were able to dupe the public about such a basic thing as the hemp plant.

They told us that cannabis hemp was a dangerous drug when indeed it is only a plant. They told us that cannabis was deadly and addictive, while doctors were filling us full of their deadly addictive chemicals and poisons. That should give you an idea of how gullible we all truly have been.

I have to give a lot of credit to people like Max Igan, David Icke, Alex Jones, and many others who have been bringing the real truth to the public about what is truly going on in this world. What they have been exposing is frightening to the average person, but we must take heed, for it is the truth.

Documentaries like *Loose Change* lays bare the corruption of the world in which we live and lets the public know who the real villains are. All of these individuals involved in supplying this information have been playing a vital role in waking the public and they are not just conspiracy theories. What they are exposing are the facts and facts cannot be denied. All you have to do is listen to what they are saying and investigate it for yourself to find the truth.

To say the world in which we live is on the wrong track is an understatement of the highest order. Still, if we act now, it is not too late to rectify the situation. Everything must be realigned to see that what is best for all forms of life and this planet takes top priority.

No longer will we allow corruption to dictate to us how we as humans must live. We are on the verge of the greatest turning point in man's history and it is essential for our future that everything is done in an open and honest manner. By proceeding in this way, a great deal can be accomplished and we can learn to work with each other to improve the lives of everyone.

If managed properly, this earth can easily sustain us all, but we must bring an end to the over production of fossil fuels and other harmful industries, which are poisoning our earth. At the same time, with the use of cannabis, starvation can be eradicated and a great number of jobs will be created in hemp-based industries to solve most of our unemployment problems.

As I have stated many times, it is our watch and it is our sacred responsibility to see that mankind will survive and prosper. Doctors will begin to follow the Hippocratic Oath and governments will begin to work for the greater good of the people. This is the only path we can follow which makes any sense and, if ignored, the destruction of the human race can be the only result.

I have been bringing the truth about this substance to the general public and to governments and all they control since 2003 but now many people are finally starting to pay attention. It has become clear to me that governments will never do the right thing unless it is forced upon them by their citizens.

Therefore, it is now left to us, the public, to remedy the situation ourselves. If governments refuse to do the right thing, then we must prevail and change government as we know it. In their place, we must appoint individuals known to be honest who have no party affiliations and no hidden agendas.

The job we are paying them for is to represent us properly. If they cannot be trusted with this sacred responsibility, then we will find someone else who can fulfill the role. You could call this strategy downsizing corruption with the aim of making everything better for everyone, except those who have caused us all this grief.

I think anyone including myself, if put in a position of public trust, should expect to have their activities while working for the public watched very closely. I can only state that indeed, the public who are paying their salaries have every right to do so to keep those who represent them honest and free of corruption.

In the past, it is more than obvious that the news media has been a dismal failure in reporting the truth to the public. If the work of those who have represented us in the past had been scrutinized by the media, as it should have been, the world in which we live would be a different place. Whatever happened to truth in journalism, did it just go out of style? Or did big money concerns simply buy the news media so they could control what the public was being told?

There is not much question that this is exactly what has happened over the last few decades. Of course, reporters knew that the public were not being given the truth about many things, but if they dared to voice an objection, their jobs would be in jeopardy. Like many other professional types, they just went along with the corruption, so they too must share the burden of guilt.

Is there anyone out there who truly does not see what has been going on and don't you think it's about time that we did something about this situation before it's too late? There is still hope, but we have to start using a great deal more common sense than we have utilized in the past.

Fortunately for us, these extracts are capable of helping people think more rationally and it even grows new brain cells in the hippocampus of those who take it as a medication. Once this oil becomes widely used, it will aid the public in thinking more clearly and they will be much harder to deceive, than they were in times gone by.

The simple truth is we are ruining this planet at an alarming rate, which in itself is bad enough, but there are also problems concerning our health which must be addressed. Babies as well as the rest of us are being given chemicals and poisons in hospitals as medicine. Every second that goes by, people are suffering and dying needlessly. Yet, we sit there and wait for what we already know to be a corrupt system to stand up and do the right thing for us all.

Truly, it can only be said, that we have been living in denial. If you want change in this world, you have to stand up and make it happen, for there is no hope that the current system will ever do it for us.

Our future and the future of everything we hold dear is at stake. Stand as one and work with us to put mankind back on the right path, then we will have accomplished something of which we all can be proud.

CHAPTER 6

HEMP MEDICINE'S POLITICAL EXILE AT LARGE

Why can the human race not seem to see what is right in front of their eyes? Or have we all been so badly brainwashed by the propaganda fed to us by the so-called system that we now lack the ability to think clearly? When it comes to hemp's medicinal use, it appears that this is indeed the case.

I used to become very angry over the behavior of politicians, doctors, lawyers, and many others concerning this issue. Still, how can we say that they must take all the blame for what has transpired? Did they not receive the same distorted propaganda and lies about this plant that we were exposed to? The obvious answer is yes; so how can we excuse ourselves and then try to hold other individuals completely at fault for the role they have played?

If many of us had been in the same positions that these individuals were, most of us would have acted no differently. We have no right to place the blame on others since they are only guilty of operating on the same faulty information which we were. The only difference between many of these individuals and ourselves is that some of us have finally come to know better. Yet, when the highly trained medical professionals we have today refuse to recognize hemp's use as a medicine, it becomes clear that something is horribly wrong with our current medical systems.

Hemp's medicinal use throughout history is legendary. For thousands of years it was used to treat practically all types of disease and injury. Only over the last few decades has hemp's medicinal use been denied to the public. To recognize the hemp plant for what it really is, all we have to do is separate fact from fiction.

The system villainized cannabis hemp to the public by renaming it marijuana. Our parents and grandparents were told by the news and movie media that the marijuana and/or hemp plant was a deadly, dangerous, and addictive drug. Nothing could have been further from the truth but back during that era it was almost impossible for the public to find out the facts for themselves.

Those who produced this ridiculous propaganda are long dead, so why do the lies and deceptions about the cannabis hemp plant still linger? The answer is simple – money. We are suffering and dying because drug companies and other big money interests want to improve their profit margins. For them to continue doing this, they must ensure that hemp is kept illegal and away from the public, for medicinal use and other purposes.

If we look into the history behind all this, we will find it was John D. Rockefeller and his rich friends along with corruption involving governments of that by-gone era which gave us the medical system we have today. In medical schools funded by the rich and powerful, doctors were taught allopathic medicine, i.e. medicine from chemicals and poisons. Over time, their lies and deceptions have convinced not only doctors, but also the general public that chemicals and poisons are beneficial for medical conditions. In other words, these so-called medical schools have brainwashed both doctors and the public at large into believing that black is white.

I hate to be the one to break the news, but chemicals and poisons are not medicine, they are simply dangerous substances which are not safe for the public to consume. Did your parents or other individuals you consider to be rational ever tell you that such things might be good for you? Or that radiation could be beneficial? When it is exposed in this fashion, a rational person has no trouble seeing the truth in what I am saying. In the distant past, such things as mercury were often used with deadly effect by those involved in what was said to be the practice of medicine.

This same insanity continues to the present day but now they have a whole new array of horrible substances with which they can harm their patients. So the use of mercury is no longer required but you can still find it in such things as vaccines.

Long before the use of all these poisonous chemicals in medicine was ever dreamed of, we had empiric medicine. Medicine from plants has been with us for thousands of years. Hemp has always been known to be the greatest empiric healer in history. In many ancient cultures, hemp was worshipped for its healing properties and was used for that purpose extensively. So how can a plant that possesses the medicinal properties of hemp continue to be denied to the public for medical purposes?

Properly produced hemp medicine is the greatest natural healer on this planet and I defy anyone to show me something that the medical system currently uses which is safer and more effective. Enough with all the medical rhetoric about double-blind testing and placebo effects. This medicine works, of that there is no doubt. If anyone from the medical establishment is willing to dispute what I am saying publicly, there are many venues on Internet programming and radio stations which would be happy to have us on the air at the same time to express our views.

How could someone like me even make these statements about this medicine if it were not true? The system would have exposed me as being a fraud years ago if they could have done so, yet, I am still here, bringing the truth to this sick and ailing world. In reality, we have all been deceived and in the end, we must all face the fact that this is the bitter truth. In addition, we must come to accept the fact that apparently we are not nearly as intelligent as we think we are, or this medical perversion could never have taken place.

All we can do is acknowledge the fact that in reality what has transpired was our own fault. Due to the ignorance concerning many subjects imposed upon the general public by their governments, we were the ones who accepted their lies, even when it went against all forms of rational thinking.

As always, I am asking governments and the medical system to do the right thing for the people. Investigate what I am saying and act upon it. In the end, we all succumb to diseases and so do our loved ones. When your turn comes, would you not want the greatest natural medicine on earth available to ease your suffering?

Everything I have ever told the public about the use of hemp medicine is true. Hemp is as history described it to be when it was referred to as being a panacea or cure-all. It is an effective control or cure for practically all diseases including cancer of all types, both internal and external. If produced properly, the essential oil of the hemp plant can replace the vast majority of pharmaceutical medications.

Now here is a medicine that is natural, non-addictive and harmless. Who in their right mind would continue to take harmful, dangerous, and addictive chemical poisons, if high quality hemp oil can solve their medical problems? As the Hippocratic Oath states, first do no harm and that is exactly what this natural medicine does. No harm.

The vast majority of people look at medicine as being some deep dark science that only doctors can understand. The simplicity and effectiveness of hemp medicine makes anyone who has it available capable of becoming their own doctor in most cases. If someone dear to you is suffering or dying, and you can simply grow a few plants that produce a harmless natural medicine which can ease their suffering and save their lives, who on earth thinks they have the right to tell you that you are not allowed to do so? Do the corporate money mongers really believe that the human race is going to continue to line up like farm animals being led to the slaughter?

Finally, the human race is starting to awaken to the reality of what the system has been doing to them. The change must come and I only hope it can be accomplished without violence. What is needed now is clear, concise, rational thinking to enable us to avoid further human suffering.

We cannot put the blame for what has taken place on the shoulders of only those who work for the system. As I have stated, we are all to blame. The vast majority of us unthinkingly do as we are told and seldom question anything the system tells us, even when we know better, so it can only be said that the fault lies within us all and that we are indeed our own worst enemy.

Now the time of change is at hand. I can only hope that big money interests will awaken to the fact that what they have been doing is completely unacceptable. The proper course of action now would be for big money interests to work with us to build a better world.

All the major hemp publications are now bringing the truth to their readers about hemp's amazing healing abilities. Testimonials concerning hemp oil's effectiveness on all types of diseases and conditions are coming out on the Internet everywhere. Hemp's medicinal use is gaining legions of supporters every day. The truth cannot and will not be held back any longer.

At the present time, hundreds of thousands of people worldwide are producing and using this wonderful medication and they are achieving the same results we did with its medicinal use. Once the restrictions are gone, this medication can be produced so cheaply that no one will need to suffer, because they do not have enough money to purchase the medicine they require.

Why are we allowing our loved ones and ourselves to suffer when there is such a simple solution? The policies of big money concerns in the past have put mankind on the wrong path, but if we work together in a sensible way, we can clean this planet up and give ourselves and coming generations a decent future. We are the human race and the future is ours to create. We can choose suffering, death, pestilence, and starvation, or we can plant hemp everywhere and use it to solve most of the problems currently facing mankind. To anyone with common sense, the choice is clear.

It is time for a radical change in the way we think. We cannot continue to poison ourselves and this planet and expect to survive. Our only salvation lies in honesty, truth, and knowledge. If we continue to accept lies and double talk, the human race will soon face extinction.

Let us give mankind a chance. Stand with me and let us put an end to all these lies and deceptions. It is our watch and it is our sacred responsibility to do so. If given the chance, Mother Earth can once again become a paradise for us all, but if the human race fails to act then it can only be said, that we are indeed the authors of our own destruction.

CHAPTER 7

MEDICINE ON THE ROCKS

I have given this article the title of "Medicine on the Rocks" for two reasons. First, because it has become more than clear that the medical system we have today is literally on the rocks morally and in practice, they are using substances and treatments that never should have been allowed for medicinal use. Secondly, due to the fact that hemp oil is a medication which actually does not need to be taken with anything else, so therefore it truly is medicine on the rocks, no mix required.

I know of no medication which is currently in use that works so effectively on all different medical conditions. Plus, this oil is harmless and non-addictive, unlike the allopathic chemicals and poisons which doctors prescribe in many cases today. It seems insane that a plant with the medical history which hemp possesses could ever have had its use restricted. Yet, to suit the agendas of the big pharmaceutical companies who wish to make huge profits, selling us their so-called safe allopathic medications, and to maintain their control over medicine, this is what has taken place.

Throughout history, cannabis has always been known as hemp by those who for thousands of years grew it as a crop. With manipulation on the part of big-money concerns and governments they control, strains of hemp with high resin content were renamed marijuana and villainized to the public at large. Back in the era when this occurred, the general public for the most part had no idea what marijuana even was. All they were told was that marijuana is a dangerous addictive and deadly drug. We were all led to believe that smoking a joint was just about the most self-destructive and harmful thing we could do to ourselves. Of course, all of this was simply just a pack of lies, but at the time, the public did not have the means to find out otherwise.

Had the public known when their governments were trying to have this plant outlawed that many of the Founding Fathers and past Presidents of the US smoked hemp quite extensively during their careers, they might not have swallowed these new restrictions that were being forced upon them so easily. There are a great number of documented accounts that describe quite vividly the smoking practices of many well-known statesmen and even how presidents like Abraham Lincoln used to enjoy the time he spent smoking hemp in his pipe sitting on his veranda.

Judging by some of the documents, political leaders of that era brought into being, such as the Declaration of Independence and the Constitution, I think it is safe to say that in fact, they were very clear thinkers. It seems that the dreaded effects of the marijuana they were smoking which the public were now being told is so detrimental, had no impact at all on such individuals or their ability to think rationally. Still, decades later when the laws restricting hemp's use were put in place in the early 1900s, very few people had knowledge of such things.

Certainly, drug companies of this era, which had been selling hemp-based medications for decades, were well aware of what marijuana really was. For these were the same varieties of hemp they had been producing their cannabis and/or hemp-based medicines from. Drug companies were more than aware of the medicinal properties of this plant, but they could not get a patent. Hemp is a plant and at that time, you could not patent a plant and nor should such a thing ever be allowed. Although the US government has been trying to say otherwise, since they put their patent in place regarding the medicinal use of this plant in 2003.

In years gone by, patenting things such as plants was not allowed, so to keep the healing power of this plant hidden, drug companies simply supplied watered-down versions of this medication and the public was never informed about its true medicinal virtues. Even in the 1800s, when drug companies such as Eli Lilly, Parke-Davis, Squibb and many others began supplying hemp-based medicines to the public, the medical virtues of this plant were well-known to them, since history had always called cannabis hemp a panacea or cure-all.

At that time, much the same as today, effective medicines were quite rare, so if drug companies wanted to sell their products, it was beneficial for their sales if they used hemp as an ingredient in their concoctions. In addition, they also sold it in other forms, such as cannabis tinctures and Eli Lilly even sold hash pills as painkillers. It is commonly known that when you are working with medicinal plants and herbs, the most medicinal aspects of such plants are brought forward when you produce the essential oils.

Therefore, of course it was common practice in the 1800s for drug companies and doctors to produce such extracts from many different medicinal plants and herbs. Since the hemp plant was known to be so medicinal, efforts must have been made to produce the essential oil from this plant also. If anyone in that era had taken the time to do so, they would be manufacturing the same substance that I have been healing everyone with. Strangely, although pharmacopeias of that time were basically wall-to-wall hemp, I have been unable to find any record of a drug company ever supplying the real essential oil of the hemp plant to the public.

Drug companies simply controlled the potency of the hemp medications they supplied so they would not have too much healing effect and looked for ways of using other substances as medicine which they could patent. I think all during this era drug companies that were producing hemp medications must have lived in fear of the general public finding out what they were doing. After all, at that time, farmers everywhere were freely growing hemp.

What would happen to the profits of drug companies if farmers found out that they could extract the most medicinal substance on earth from the plants they were already growing? Indeed, if such a thing had occurred, the drug industry would have had a very bleak future.

Then in the early 1900s, individuals who go by names like Rockefeller started medical foundations, which taught the use of allopathic medicine, since mixtures of chemicals and poisons can be patented. There was little profit to be found in the old tried and true empiric approach, which produces medications from plants. So in their never-ending quest to increase their piece of the pie, drug companies took the allopathic approach, because that's where the money could be made. What difference did it make to them morally or otherwise that such substances do harm to the human body, when it appears that all they were really interested in was making more money for themselves? In time, after the right palms had been greased, they succeed in having the governments and parties that they already controlled restrict hemp's medicinal use entirely.

Just give good old hemp a name like marijuana and tell the masses through deceptive propaganda that it's a dangerous and deadly new drug and the populous might be ignorant enough about the subject to allow these restrictions to be put in place.

In no time, this is what transpired and parents were then scared to death that their children would come into contact with the dreaded reefer man. This is how gullible and misinformed people in that era were and many individuals today, it seems, are still suffering from this same affliction.

Everyone, tends to overlook the fact that no one ever died or has been seriously harmed from using hemp as a medicine. This, plus the fact that it is so medicinally active, should have ensured that its medical use would never be restricted. It was simply the blind trust, we all seem to have for those in positions of authority that has provided us with the medical madness we endure today.

I still have a certain amount of respect for dentists and surgeons, or at least the ones which are good at plying their trade. But as far as the rest of the medical system goes, I feel that there is obviously a great deal of room left for improvement. After learning the truth about this profession, I now look at most doctors as nothing more than legalized drug dealers for the big pharmaceutical companies.

Practically everything the doctors provide us with are liver toxic poisons and chemicals that are often very addictive in nature. In addition, they provide chemo and radiation that they try to tell us could help if we are diagnosed with cancer or other serious conditions.

Anyone with two working brain cells knows that poison, chemicals and radiation are harmful, but still, people line up like sheep for their so-called treatments. If your own mother put on a white coat and tried to tell you that toxic substances and radiation are beneficial, you would think she was out to do you harm, or that possibly she had gone completely off the deep end.

Yet, since it is your trusted doctor that is now giving you this same advice, you meekly do as you're told and often even thank them for harming you. Practically every treatment doctors provide goes against their own Hippocratic Oath, which makes them nothing more than dealers in death. Yet, the vast majority of us appear to think that we don't have the right to question the authority of a doctor. If I gave someone poison and they died from its effects, you would call me a murderer. Yet, if a doctor does the same and brings about the death of a patient with the use of their poisons, it is then called medicine.

In reality, what hospitals and doctors are doing today could easily be considered nothing more than a mass extermination project, which is very similar in nature to what Hitler did in his death camps, but it is being done on a grander scale and in a much more insidious way.

Very often, medicine today is not about healing any longer, it now in reality for the most part concerns the ability to produce huge profits. There would be very little money to be made by drug companies if they provided natural medicines which actually healed you. So instead they often provide addictive chemicals and poisons that do harm to keep you coming back for more. To them, it's just good business, but to those of us who have nowhere to turn and must take their treatments, the future is quite grim.

If we actually had governments that were really running our countries honestly and working for the greater good of their people, none of this would be taking place. Instead, in most cases, all we have to represent us are bought and paid for lackeys that could best be described as being little more than yes men, for the system that is oppressing us. Although one must give them credit for their acting skills, we have to realize that these are individuals, who are only making a lame attempt in trying to deceive us into believing that they are truly representing our best interests.

With all the attention this oil is currently receiving all over the globe, by now many of those in government circles must obviously know the truth. So in fact they are now working in league with the big-money concerns to try to keep things the way they are, to maintain the old status quo. While many others who still currently stand against this medication's use could only be said to be badly misinformed about their opinions, but in reality they are probably little different than you or I.

Sadly, it seems, that they are simply individuals who were brought up to believe all the negative propaganda about this plant. Then due to some flaw in their genetic makeup, or possibly a lack of cannabinoids in their systems, which would do nothing to help one think more clearly, they are unable to reject the lies they were told in favor of the truth.

The excuses they have come up with to try to prevent cannabis hemp from being used medicinally by us all are simply outrageous. We often hear things like they are trying to take the high out, then they will be able to use it as a medicine. Look at the high people receive from other drugs produced by the pharmaceutical industry, not only that, look at their dangerous addictive natures.

If you take an overdose of many of their so-called medications, you could easily find yourself in a morgue. That's the reason somewhere around 80% of drug-related deaths reported from street use are caused from pharmaceuticals. How many people do you know that have died from an overdose of hemp and why would any thinking person want to take the high out of this medication? In hospitals, the high that morphine and other opiate-based medications provide is used to kill pain, but they are very addictive and if you take a little too much, you are on a one-way trip to the graveyard.

Still, medications like this are produced and sold by drug companies with no consideration for the danger or addiction they present. Since the drug industry legally produces these substances, they are used freely, often much too freely, judging by the number of needless deaths which have been attributed to their effects.

Now let's have a look at the "devastating" effects of a very large overdose of hemp oil. This medication causes a semi-comatose condition called sleep and, when produced from the right strains, it is also a much more effective painkiller than morphine ever was. If an ordinary person were to take far too much, no doubt, they would sleep for quite some time, but when they awoke, they would be unharmed and suffer no addiction.

I have provided this medication to many patients, yet I do not know of any condition that would prevent a patient from using this substance to good advantage; still, in time we may find that there are those who cannot. All I am saying is that I know of no medication that is more effective and safe to use and I'm sure the medical system, uses nothing which they can say the same about. Now look at the effects of hemp oil and look at the effects of what the medical system provides. I think you will agree that taking the high out of hemp medications is just about the lamest excuse that they could have come up with, when you consider the harmful and dangerous nature of substances they are presently using to take its place.

It seems most doctors and the system which controls their profession, knowingly or otherwise, are more than happy to turn their backs on the ugly truth that is staring them in the face. Therefore, governments and all they control, be it the medical or legal system etc., are all working against the public's well-being. Why do they do such things when it's obvious so much harm is being done? The reason lies in our own self-destructive nature and the desire of many, who wish to dominate others.

Obviously, what politicians, doctors, lawyers, police officers etc. are doing is wrong. Yet, you can take almost anyone and put them in a position of authority and you will find that most will behave in the same manner. The sad truth is most will do whatever they are told, as long as someone is paying them enough money. Individuals in such positions seem to think that they are not responsible for the government policies they are upholding and their standard reply is, "We are just doing our jobs." So, to them, filling us full of chemicals and kicking in our doors to steal the hemp we are growing for our own medicinal needs is perfectly rational behavior.

It seems that under the right circumstances most of us have the ability to turn our backs on reality, especially if we are being well rewarded for our actions. Who cares if what the system is doing is having a harmful effect on this planet and all forms of life it supports, including our own? As long as they give us enough money and tell us we are not responsible, the world is our oyster, but if in reality we are not responsible, then who is?

For example, how could anyone truly feel justified in thinking that it is within their jurisdiction or indeed should be considered part of their duty to confiscate a natural medication from someone who needs it to preserve their life? Most people find it hard to comprehend but this type of thing is taking place every day and it is not only the police, who are showing no empathy or compassion.

In truth, the same could be said about the actions of countless individuals who have been put in positions of authority. Then, when they are asked to perform their duties in an honest way, as they had sworn to do. The greed and corruption within their own professions, which is interlinked to government controls, prevents them from doing so. After realizing that speaking out in most cases does little good and indeed, could put their future in jeopardy, the vast majority of those who are supposed to be working in positions of public trust will quickly master the art of remaining silent

Sadly, in too many cases, this is the way most of us behave because we are all trying to get ahead and to do this, we must have a good paying job. For most who are trying to work within a system that is so badly corrupted, it is much easier to just go with the flow and do as you are told by your superiors. Welcome to Orwell's world of Big Brother, only this time it's for real and they are presently in control of just about everything.

Yet, even at this late date, it can still be rectified. We have to awaken the public to the danger of what is presently confronting them. Those who are now in control must be stripped of the right they seem to think they have to guide humanity's destiny. We don't want the genetically modified foods, or their Codex Alimentarius, we want the freedom and right to choose for ourselves. We also demand our right to honest representation, which has been badly lacking in the past. No matter if the so-called system likes it or not, we are the people and when we speak out as one, we have the power to guide our own destiny.

I don't know about others, but I would like to see our children have a decent future. But what future could they possibly have in a world run by power-hungry and greedy individuals, who don't even seem to understand the meaning of the word compassion? The future is ours to create but let us put the decision-making in the hands of wise and honest individuals and let's bring an end to the psychopathic agenda of those who are presently in control. Our aim should not be to seek retribution but to simply bring about change by whatever means that are deemed necessary.

It's hard to believe that a simple innocent plant could actually destroy the corruption which has been plaguing our world for so long. Yet, in the end, that is exactly what this plant will do, and it will also provide the human race with a whole different way of life. Your job in the pill factory or oil fields may be gone, but there will be a great deal of employment provided in the new hemp-based industries which will begin to take root everywhere and finally we can then start to do things in a much more earth-friendly way.

As I understand it, today over 50,000 different items can be produced from hemp but in my book, medicine, ending starvation, and providing energy are at the top of the list. As Jack Herer, the Emperor of Hemp himself said, "I don't know if hemp will save the world but I do know it's the only thing that can." These are wise words from a great man who sadly is no longer with us, but his words ring true and it's time that we all begin to take his advice.

Any doctor who stands against hemp's free medicinal use is either badly misinformed or they are simply quacks, who are prescribing chemicals to enrich themselves and their masters the big drug firms. In most cases, hemp's use as a medicine requires no supervision by a doctor and this is something they consider to be a great threat to their profession. In reality, since this medication is so safe, why could we simply not just treat ourselves and determine our own doses, no doctor required.

We should all have the natural right to have a large jar of high-grade hemp oil at home to take care of our family's medicinal needs. By allowing this, if something were to happen such as a burn, the patient could be put under treatment instantly and this in return would reduce a great deal of needless suffering, plus the patient would heal much more rapidly.

If you grow the plants yourself, this medication can be produced for practically nothing. For those who find it impossible to produce their own extracts, governments should supply their needs on a donation basis. That way, even if you have no funding, you would still receive the medication you require. In addition, if the oil is made freely available, it will put an end to the use of practically all the dangerous drugs which are currently prescribed today. The use of hemp as a medication also presents no danger to your children. So if I were you, I would get them off any chemicals they are currently taking, before it does them any more harm.

This medication can be ingested, used topically, vaporized, or you are also able to use it in suppository form with good results. When you begin ingesting these extracts, little tiny doses taken about eight hours apart are best in the beginning. If you're suffering from a serious condition and you are taking strong pain medications, increase the size of your dosage as quickly as possible and try to discontinue the use of these dangerous substances.

For those who think they need guidance, since your doctor was the one who put you on all these addictive nasty chemicals in the first place, ask them for their advice on how to best discontinue the use of these substances. If your own doctor is unwilling to help, see a naturopath or homeopathic practitioner for advice. In many cases in the past, I have seen people go off unneeded medications all by themselves with no advice from anyone.

Upon commencing treatment with the oil, many patients who are taking opiate-based medications, can instantly cut their use of these dangerous substances in half. In most cases, within one to two weeks the patient can get off these medications entirely and they will suffer much less withdrawal symptoms.

Very often I'm asked if the oil will work for many different medical conditions and the answer is yes, from what I've seen, these extracts can be effective for all conditions. If you have produced high-grade oil from the proper strains, it promotes full body healing in all respects. You almost have to see the healing power of this substance with your own eyes, since in many cases it can actually defy description. From my perspective, I do not really feel that we need more time-consuming research to find out if this medication actually works.

After providing this oil to thousands of people to treat their different medical conditions, I can tell you firsthand that it does. Much of the evidence I had gathered disappeared after the police raids on my property, but now there should be more than enough testimonials up on the internet to prove what I am saying is true.

In the future, what we need to do is grow the most medicinal strains in a controlled environment. Then, using a simple process of elimination, we will be able to determine which oils from different strains or mix of different oils, are the most effective to treat different conditions.

Since most of the strong indica and highly indica-dominant sativa crosses are so medicinal, we can be healing those who are suffering, while finding out what we need to know. To many people, hemp is simply one thing, but I call it the plant with a thousand medicinal profiles. Each oil produced from different strains will vary in their medicinal values, so that's where the research is needed.

Even people with thought-to-be incurable diseases can now have hope of making a recovery. Over the years, we have had great results in the treatment of MS, AIDS, arthritis, diabetes, glaucoma, chronic pain, all forms of cancer, and everything else. Many times, I have seen this oil successfully treat conditions that the medical system didn't even have a name for. Yes indeed, folks, medicine as we've always known it is about to be stood on its head. For now we have a natural harmless medication, at our fingertips that really does amazing healing abilities.

The beauty in all this is, hemp oil is something we can all supply ourselves with very easily. At the present time, hundreds of thousands, if not millions worldwide, are doing just that and the healing power of this oil is gaining more recognition every day. The system can use all the negative propaganda they want, to try to maintain control and to keep hemp's medicinal use restricted. Yet, how can this still be accomplished when people are seeing their friends and neighbors healed with the use of this wonderful oil? The clock is ticking and soon now, this system's reign of terror will soon be over and then it will be left to us all to build a better world.

Coming from a small backwater town like Springhill, Nova Scotia and ending up living as an exile in Europe has been quite a journey. At one point in time, I was the proverbial proud Canadian, but due to what I have discovered, I can no longer express this view, for in reality there is little to be proud of when you know that your government is actively participating in genocide against its own people. They feed us all this nonsense about freedom and democracy, while sending young men and women to fight, kill, and often be killed in wars fought over money and control, thereby committing genocide against other nations as well.

Like most, until a few years ago, I was living in ignorance as to what has been going on and I thought that Canada was a great country. Then, in 2001, I started to find out about the healing abilities of these extracts and after doing so, I then went on a campaign to bring the truth out. I went to all the right people in all the right places, yet I found that none of them was really interested in finding or bringing out a cure for anything.

Indeed, it seemed that no one wanted to support the use of this medication at all, except the poor patients who were suffering with severe medical problems. After realizing that no one in authority intended to do anything, it really didn't take too long to figure out that those in positions of trust could not be trusted. So I just continued on supplying the oil to patients, thinking that sooner or later, the government or someone in authority would have to come to their senses.

Right from the very beginning, I knew the impact this medication would have, so I was hoping that the government would work with me to bring this to the public in a rational way. I even went to the newspapers long before I was ever charged by the RCMP, so it was certainly no secret about what I was doing. Then they sent the RCMP in to try to bring my activities to a halt. There were 1620 plants taken from my backyard in the summer of 2005 and I was arrested and charged. Then, in the summer of 2006, they came back and took 1100 plants more, although this time I was not arrested.

The news media put out jaded articles about what was going on but from what they stated it was more than obvious that they too were controlled, since they never printed or presented the real truth about what was taking place. Even the Royal Canadian Legion got involved and in the end proved that they also were taking part in the government's corruption. It seemed no matter where we turned with this issue, doors were slammed in our faces.

Then in the pursuit of justice, I was brought into court where I had the misfortune of witnessing the actions of the so-called Canadian legal system. First, it was decided that I should mount a Charter challenge. Under the Charter of Rights and Freedoms currently in place in Canada, it clearly states that we all have the right to life. Even though I presented 48 affidavits from patients who had used this medication to treat their conditions, the judge simply stated that they were anecdotal and said I presented no life-threatening conditions.

This of course made no sense, since skin cancer and post-concussion syndrome can both be very life-threatening. In addition, what right does a judge with no medical background even have to make such determinations and how could he say that affidavits concerning the use of a medicinal plant that has been used for 5000 years in medicine are anecdotal?

In the end, they proved to me that due to their corruption, the charter of rights and freedoms, is not being upheld. According to the Canadian legal system which I had the misfortune of dealing with, we only have the right to use their so-called medications. Being allowed access to man's oldest known and safest medication was totally out of the question. Since this is what took place, it seems to me that either the Charter of Rights and Freedoms is a total fraud, or the judge that presided over my case should be sent to prison himself, because he did not uphold my rights as a Canadian citizen.

We then proceeded on with my case in the Supreme Court of Nova Scotia with the same judge and prosecutors that had handled my Charter challenge. Of course, by this time the judge and those who were prosecuting me were all well aware of the fact that everything I was saying was true. Knowing that they were persecuting an innocent man, who was just trying to do something good for mankind, did not seem to bother them in the least.

The prosecution led off putting several police officers on the stand who had taken part in the raid but I was able to destroy their credibility during the cross-examination, since they all had to testify that I had approached the use of this medication in such an open and honest way. A year before I was ever charged, I had gone to the newspapers about all of this and the officers that testified had to admit that no criminal would even consider doing such a thing.

In addition, I had provided the RCMP with videotaped evidence showing how effective this medication was and had asked them if they could give me all the hemp they confiscated, so I could produce more medicine. In the same video, I also informed the RCMP that I was growing hemp in my backyard, so I could treat those who were suffering. All this took place in May 2005, three months before I was ever charged, so no one can say that I was trying to hide anything. After the prosecution was done with their segment of the trial, the case they had tried to present was not very convincing.

I had ten patients and six doctors ready to give testimony, but of course, none of them were allowed to testify because the judge said their testimony had nothing to do with my case. Patients cured of terminal cancer and other serious medical problems ready to testify, but this judge had the nerve to say that their testimony could not be heard.

Then I was not allowed to present any of the scientific evidence we had gathered because the authors of these research studies were not present in the court. So, in the end, I was the only one allowed to testify in my own defense, which I think I did quite effectively.

It really appears that this must have been the case, for in the end the crown prosecutor even had to stoop to jury tampering to see that I was found guilty. There were people on that jury whose relatives this oil had healed and I charged them nothing for the treatment, yet I was found guilty. Guilty of what? Healing?

There is no question in my mind that this judge, the two prosecutors and the jury which heard this case, have a great deal of blood on their hands. In Canada, about 70,000 people are dying from cancer each year, not to mention the tens of thousands more who are dying and suffering from other conditions, which this oil is effective in treating.

This means that from 2003 until the present, over 900,000 people have died in Canada from cancer alone. I am not saying that we could have saved them all, but no doubt, we could have saved a great many from this fate, if we had only been given the chance. Cancer is just one disease that is taking its toll in Canada. Now imagine all the rest who died from other conditions which could have been helped by this oil's use. I know genocide is a very strong word, but what else can you call what is currently taking place in Canada and elsewhere? Sadly, this has been going on for a very long time, but in the near future patients will finally have access to a natural medication that really does work.

The jury tampering committed by the crown prosecutor and witnessed by Margret Dwyer was never disproved and they basically refused, to properly investigate what had taken place. The judge simply dismissed it all by stating that this was just something the lady who had witnessed the event and I, had cooked up to derail my sentencing. This proved once more to me that those who are supposed to be upholding the law, are in reality doing just the opposite.

After all this nonsense in court, I was given a $2000 fine and a gun restriction, although I have no idea why such a restriction was put in place, since there was no firearms present in my home when the raids were conducted. The RCMP were the only ones threatening people's lives and waving guns around, so wouldn't the public be better served, if some restrictions were put in place regarding their behavior?

After my case was over, all I wanted to do was get out of Canada, but people kept coming to me looking for help, so I just continued doing the same as I had been all along and after a while it seemed that I was going to be left alone. Finally, the hemp publications became involved and I was asked to come to Europe to speak on the subject. In October 2009, I spent three weeks in Europe on a speaking tour after which I then returned home.

Then on November 20, 2009, I returned to Amsterdam to attend the Cannabis Cup where I put on a seminar and was crowned Freedom Fighter of the Year. Just before I was presented with this award, I received word that once again my property back in Canada had been raided by the RCMP. I had grown hemp right in my backyard again in 2009 and since I announced its presence on a popular maritime radio talk show in June of 2009, everyone including the RCMP knew it was there. Instead of raiding me like they had done in past years, this time they stayed away with their helicopters. Then, once the crop had been processed into medicine and distributed to those in need, I returned to Europe to attend the Cannabis Cup.

It seems to be somewhat suspicious to me, but this was when the RCMP chose to strike, after all the cannabis was gone and I had departed for Europe. The RCMP are well known for their attempts to frame individuals whose activities are making their government uncomfortable, so it appears they sent the right flunkies who have no sense of right and wrong to complete the mission.

When I heard what they planned to charge me with, it was so ridiculous that their so-called charges were almost laughable. I think I was striking such a sore spot with the government of Canada that they might have thought that bringing bogus charges against me, would prevent me from returning. After witnessing the disgraceful behavior, I had seen in the past from all that the Canadian government controls, I must admit that they were quite right in making this assumption.

I don't think the dishonest individuals who are in control of the land of my birth had realized just how well known this issue and myself had become. If I went back to Canada, I knew the corruption I would have to face again and I also knew that I would probably be put in jail without my medication. So, for me, returning to Canada would be something similar to committing suicide, since I need this medication which they would deny, to survive.

From my perspective, I could fight their corruption from over here just as well anyway, so I decided to remain in Europe. It's been a bit of a rough ride over here at times, but I have come to like living in many of these foreign lands and I have also been given the opportunity to meet some very interesting individuals.

Then on April 15, 2010 Jack Herer passed away and his dying wish was, that he wanted me to take over the leadership of the hemp movement in his place. Our documentary "Run from the Cure" produced by Christian Laurette of Amherst, Nova Scotia had caught the attention of the Emperor of Hemp himself, just shortly after it had been released in early 2008. This documentary was produced on a shoestring budget, but somehow Christian did the impossible and managed to piece together a very good documentary. It may not have been a big Hollywood production, but Jack Herer certainly knew the truth when it was put before him.

A short time later, Jack called me from California and he and I became the best of friends. After getting to know him I appeared on the Internet shows Jack used to do many times. Jack's views on different issues and my own were so close it was almost as if we were the same person. Although I was basically an unknown, this great man treated me as an equal.

I didn't realize it at the time because to me Jack and I were just good friends who thought about the same on most subjects. But it seems that Jack was looking at me as more than just a friend. It appears he was thinking of me as a replacement for himself and he expressed these views to Steve Hager shortly before he collapsed from a heart attack.

So upon Jack's death, the leadership of the hemp movement was placed in my hands according to Jack's wishes. I have, so to speak, stepped into Jack's shoes, but in reality, no one can replace Jack, for he was the one and only Emperor of Hemp. Stepping up to the plate in Jack's place comes with many responsibilities, but since the free medicinal use of this plant and the hemp movement go hand-in-hand, thus far I've been able to manage without too much difficulty.

Being the new leader of the movement has been of some aid in getting the truth out to people more easily. This knowledge is now spreading so rapidly that soon it will be worldwide and recognized by everyone. Since I have more or less been stranded in Europe, I have continued to speak about this issue as often as possible. In reality, I have adjusted quite well to the unsettled life I have been leading and I have come to look at seeing Europe up close and personal, as being somewhat of an adventure.

Still, my forced absence has been very hard on my friends and loved ones back home. To me, it's almost as if I don't know where home is anymore, but now I really do feel that I probably will never live in Canada again on a steady basis. It's not that I don't love my homeland, it's simply because the growing season in Canada is quite short and there is far too much corruption there for me to deal with. Many countries in warmer climates have much better conditions, so put simply, I could achieve my goals more easily living somewhere else.

Years ago, Leonard Cohen had to leave Canada and travel to France to become a popular recording artist. Now I too had to leave Canada to produce the oil and find a government that will do the right thing for mankind. It's a shame the Canadian government chose the path they did, for Canada could have been the country that introduced the amazing healing power of this plant to the world. Now that honor will likely go to the Czech Republic or some other nation.

The government of whatever nation, which chooses to act, will in a short time be honored for being the first to do what's right for the human race. When this occurs, how will the Canadian government be looked at by the rest of the world and what about the American government who have obviously known the true medicinal value of this plant, since at least the 1970's? In the coming months I expect that there will be many scandals exposed and vast numbers of those who are now standing against this medication's use will suddenly become tongue-tied and unable to speak.

For the time being, it seems that I have my work cut out for me over here, so I will try to educate as many as possible until our goal is achieved. There are now many research projects ready to get underway in some countries, so I expect the coming months for me will be very busy and exciting times. The winds of change are not only blowing, now they are beginning to howl. When this medication goes back into mainstream medicinal use, all will change and any corruption regarding this issue will be a thing of the past. I wish everyone back home in Canada the very best and want them all to know that soon now we will have a much healthier and brighter future. Yet, the time it takes to accomplish this would be greatly reduced if we simply just stood as one and demanded our natural right to the medicinal use of this greatest of all healing herbs.

I have challenged the medical system and governments on many occasions to do an honest and open review of this medication before the public. But to date, the system has avoided doing so and have simply carried on with their lies and doubletalk. If all I have been telling everyone about the healing abilities of this plant is not true, then the government and medical system should be more than happy to openly disprove what I have been saying, before the general public. Since the information I have brought forward is the truth and government is fully aware of this fact, it is highly unlikely that my challenge will ever be met or even considered. This should prove to everyone just who is on the up and up and in the end you will find it is not your government.

What is to happen in the future is truly now in the hands of us all. If you care nothing about the health and welfare of your friends and loved ones and you are willing to let those without a conscience guide your future, all you have to do is just sit there and continue to do as you are told. But if you care about this earth and the well-being of all the creatures that inhabit this planet and coming generations, you must speak out about this issue and demand that those in authority begin working for the greater good of us all. The truth must be brought forward and the lies and propaganda of the past ignored. The health and happiness of everyone we know is at stake, and so it is now our responsibility as human beings to begin acting properly. In reality, we all want to live long healthy lives and this is exactly what high quality essential oils from the right strains of cannabis hemp can provide.

This medication is really not about getting you high, it's about allowing yourself to become healed by a natural substance that does no harm. Now why should we as humans allow others to continue denying us the use of this medication? The free medicinal use of hemp is the most important issue of our time and since so many are dying needlessly, all other concerns pale by comparison. Hemp is medicine for the masses that practically anyone can grow and produce. Now countless people worldwide are producing their own medication and they are achieving the same results we have described in our information. The time for change is now at hand, please join with us to help end the suffering of so many people and to bring hope to an otherwise hopeless world.

CHAPTER 8

THE EMPEROR'S APPRENTICE

I first came into contact with Jack Herer in 2008 when he got in touch with me and expressed an interest in my work. Jack told me when he first viewed our documentary "Run from the Cure" that he felt like he had been run over by a truck. He stated, with his knowledge of this plant, he could not believe that he himself had not realized the hemp plant's healing potential.

As soon as Jack watched our documentary, he quickly came to the conclusion that what we were saying had to be true. He already knew cannabis hemp certainly had healing powers, but until I came along, no one had ever released information concerning the medicinal use of the essential oil which can be produced from this plant. Whatever healing abilities any particular variety of hemp has will be concentrated into the essential oil when it is produced. All this made perfect sense to Jack and, like me, he knew the only way this plant would once again be recognized for the wonder it is, would be to prove its medical virtues to the public.

To help achieve this aim, I appeared on Jack's Internet show many times and I thoroughly enjoyed the experience. Unfortunately, Jack and I never did get to meet face to face, but through our many phone conversations, we became the best of friends. Jack's views on this subject and mine were very similar, so I guess that's why he told Steve Hager from High Times magazine, if anything happened to him that the torch was to be passed on to me.

After Jack collapsed with a heart attack in September 2009, I tried to fill in for him until he recovered, but in reality, no one could ever replace Jack. Sadly, a few months later, the hemp movement lost its heart and soul when Jack passed away. All of this occurred under very strange circumstances and I strongly suspect foul play could have been involved. When Jack was in the hospital, he was denied the use of the oil and even his wife Jeannie was not allowed in to see him. So, to me, something does not seem right about all this.

In the spring of 2009, a few months before Jack took the heart attack, he contacted me to write a chapter for the upcoming 12th edition of the Emperor Wears No Clothes. I sent the chapter to Jack and, after going over it, he called me back and said he had given it his OK. The 12th edition came out a few months after Jack's passing, and when I saw it, I was shocked. This was not the same book I had come to have such respect for. It was about 100 pages shorter than the original and the chapter I had sent to Jack was not to be found. It wasn't the fact that the chapter I had written was not published that bothered me so much, although it would have been very beneficial to many if this information had been included. Instead, it was the disrespect I felt those who re-edited the original book had shown Jack when they changed his original manuscript.

Death is forever and when we lose someone like Jack, our world seems to become a colder and more inhospitable place to dwell. People like Jack bring hope into our lives that possibly we could live in a much better and different way. So, the passing of someone like Jack Herer has an adverse effect on us all and it's very hard to find someone who would be a suitable replacement for such a man.

After Steve Hager told those who attended Jack's funeral service that Jack had wanted me to replace him, I could do little else but try to abide by his wishes. Although it was truly an honor to be named as Jack's replacement, I really felt I had little time to take on the role that Jack had played, since I was already so busy on the medicinal front. Still, when the Emperor speaks, he must be obeyed, so I have stepped into his role and tried to do my best. I find what I am now doing to be rather strange, since the movement Jack made me the leader of will hopefully become unnecessary and redundant. Once the injustice that has been done to the public and this plant has been rectified, I will be out of a job. Perhaps when this occurs, I will be able to get back to the serious research on this plant, which I still consider to be so important.

Recently, Jeannie Herer got in touch and said she would like to include what I had written in the new audio book of the Emperor Wears No Clothes, which she was then working on. Since the chapter she had asked for was now among the missing and many things have changed over the last three years, I had to completely rewrite the entire chapter to bring it up to date. But I am thrilled Jeannie wanted the chapter I have written included in the audio book and I'm sure Jack would be very pleased as well.

Jack Herer was not only my friend; he was also my hero and mentor and I consider him to be the greatest leader the hemp movement has ever known. Even though he is no longer with us to act as our guide, we need to see that the dream he had for us all becomes a reality. People must be free to heal themselves naturally and cannabis hemp produces the greatest natural medicine on earth. Since hemp presents no danger to the public, it goes without saying that the time for this medication's use is now. People are suffering and dying needlessly all over the globe, now why don't we put an end to their misery? If indeed we are truly human, we can do no less.

What is taking place in the field of hemp research at present is truly a nightmare. People are making all kinds of claims to sell their ideas and products. This will only continue to get worse until the proper research is done, with no interference from governments and those who control them.

In the meantime, I want the public to know that there are many scam artists out there and some have even been using my name to fatten their bank accounts. So at present it's ´buyer beware´ and if you want the real thing, it's best to produce your own oil, for at least then you will know what you have. The instructions on how to produce the oil are available on my website at www.phoenixtears.ca and also in my book which is called The Rick Simpson Story available at www.simpsonramadur.com.

Some people are afraid to produce the oil themselves, but once they do, they quickly realize it's really not much harder than making a cup of coffee. The most important thing is to find some very potent heavily sedative starting material, preferably with 20% THC or more, to produce this medication in the proper way. Then, it's just a matter of following the instructions and in three or four hours the medicine is sitting there ready to use.

When I was producing the oil on a large scale, I didn't have chemists and laboratories at my disposal. Still, the oil I produced had the desired effect and thousands were healed, who had been suffering from serious medical conditions. If I can do all this by myself at home, I see no reason that most people cannot do the same. It may be an inconvenience to many, but until suppliers start practicing quality control and there are standards in place, it is much more sensible to produce your own medication.

This all began for me when I watched my 25-year-old cousin die a horrible death from cancer in 1972. At that time, cancer was still quite rare and my cousin David was the first person I knew directly who died from this disease.

About three years after his death, I heard a report on the radio, which stated THC, the active ingredient in marijuana, has been found to kill cancer cells. While the announcer was making these statements, he was laughing like a fool, so I thought this report might be his idea of a practical joke. As time went on, I heard nothing more about THC killing cancer cells, but for some reason, the report I had listened to stayed in my memory. Many years later, the report I had heard would be instrumental in saving both my life and the lives of many others.

I spent most of my working career employed as a power engineer at All Saints Hospital in Springhill, Nova Scotia. In 1997, I suffered a severe head injury that left me with a condition called post-concussion syndrome. My injury caused an unbearable high-pitched ringing sound in my head 24 hours a day, which affected my blood pressure badly. My injury also left me with balance problems and other issues that required medical attention.

I spent years going from doctor to doctor, but all the chemicals they gave me did nothing to improve my situation. In fact, many of the prescriptions I was provided with came with horrible side effects, that were just as bad or worse than what I was being treated for. In late 1998, I watched an episode of The Nature of Things with Dr. David Suzuki called Reefer Madness II. In this broadcast, they showed many people who were finding relief from their medical problems by simply smoking cannabis. I had smoked pot in the past, but I had never looked at it as being a medicine, so I acquired a small amount and sure enough, it worked much better than anything the doctors supplied.

Immediately, I started asking doctors for a prescription, so I could use this substance legally. When I inquired about hemp, I received replies like "It's still under study," or "Smoking pot is bad for your lungs." At the time, I thought doctors must have a good reason for withholding the use of this medication, so I continued to take their chemicals and trash. Smoking cannabis was far more effective in helping me sleep than what the doctors had provided. Yet, it still didn't have the power to knock me out so I could get the rest I needed.

One day in 1999, I was in my doctor's office and asked him what he would think if I produced the essential oil from the hemp plant and ingested it as a medication as opposed to just smoking pot. The doctor got a strange look on his face, but agreed that this would be a much more medicinal way to use the substance. Yet, still, he would not provide a prescription, so I could use the substance legally. Finally, in 2001, my doctor told me there wasn't anything further he could do, he had tried everything at his disposal and nothing helped, so I was now on my own. Again, I asked to be given a prescription for hemp, but was promptly refused.

By this time, the chemicals I had been given had more or less turned me into a zombie. I couldn't think clearly and did not seem to be able to remember anything. Even though my thinking abilities were not at their best, I could not help but wonder what these doctors were doing. They had passed out addictive and dangerous chemicals to me like they were going out of style. Yet, when I approached them to give me a prescription for hemp which is non-addictive and harmless, I was promptly denied. Something was going on here that didn't make any sense to me, but it would take a while longer for me to discover what they were hiding.

When I first started taking the oil as my only medication, I was scared to death of the substance, because I had no idea what it would really do. I started with little tiny doses that had about the same effect as smoking a joint. The only difference was that instead of being instant, it would take about an hour for the effects of the oil to be felt. Once I started to step up my dosage, down I went. This substance could knock an elephant off its feet. I started getting from eight to twelve hours of solid sleep every night and my condition began to rapidly improve.

In the beginning, I didn't know what was happening. My thinking processes were improving, but I was losing weight at an alarming rate. I didn't know it at the time, but the oil was simply detoxifying my body and bringing me back to a healthy weight. Not much wonder I was a bit mixed up about what the oil was doing, for who would have believed the essential oil from a plant could do such a thing? Not only that, but the oil was controlling my blood pressure and my balance issues were showing improvement every day. Of course, this likely had something to do with the fact that I was no longer taking the chemicals. As the toxins from these medications were flushed from my system, my balance problems improved dramatically.

The oil worked in so many ways it took me quite some time to comprehend all that it was doing for my overall health. Shortly after I began taking this substance, the arthritis in my knees, which I had suffered from since I was forty five years old, just disappeared. Then, I was reminded of something that had happened when I first tried to make the oil under the influence of the medications I was given by the medical system. Since my thinking was impaired, I somehow managed to set myself on fire and being a human torch is not a pleasant experience. My right hand got the worst of it and by the time the fire was extinguished, three quarters of my hand was hanging in big gobs. My right hand was now literally deep-fried.

Third-degree burns like this do not heal easily and always leave horrible scars. In eleven days, my right hand was completely healed, leaving no scars. At the time, the chemicals I was taking had scattered my brain so badly, that when my hand had healed this quickly, I just dismissed what I had witnessed by telling myself I must be a good healer. I know how stupid all this sounds, but this is the effect these powerful chemical medications can have on our brains and I was no exception.

Within a very short time, the oil had brought me back to a state of decent health, but I had three areas on my body, which I suspected were skin cancer. I had been having problems with these areas for years but had not mentioned them to my doctor. I guess I didn't want to admit to myself that I probably had cancer and by not telling him I could continue to live the fantasy. Finally, in late 2002, I pointed them out and the doctor said they looked like skin cancer, but he wouldn't know for sure until he received a copy of my pathology report. The area he expressed the most concern about was on the side of my nose close to my right eye. The doctor said they would deal with that area first and they could take care of the lesions on my chest and left cheek at a later date.

About a week after the surgery had been performed, I was examining what they had done when the report I had heard almost 30 years before popped back into my mind. By this time, I had been taking the oil for quite a while and this caused me to question the report I had heard. If THC kills cancer cells, why had it not worked in my case? After all the oil I had taken, my system must be full of THC, I thought. I was quite doubtful about all this, but to prove it, there was only one thing I could do. I decided to apply oil directly to the other areas that had been giving me problems and cover them with a bandage. I left the bandages in place for four days and there was no sensation that anything was happening. So, when I removed the bandages, I was shocked to see that the cancer was completely gone and all that remained was healthy pink skin.

I started telling those I knew well that I thought the oil had cured my cancer, but they laughed at me and blew it off like it was nothing. Then a few weeks later, the cancer that had been surgically removed close to my eye returned. I treated the area the same way I did the others and, four days later, it, too, was completely healed. Now the only question which remained was could it really have been cancer that I had treated?

A few days later I went to my doctor's office for a copy of my pathology report and the specimen they tested after my operation proved that I had basal cell carcinoma. I told the receptionist the cancer next to my eye had returned and that I treated this and the other two areas that were giving me problems with hemp oil and now they were healed. I wanted to come back in the evening and talk to the doctor about what had taken place, but his receptionist said the doctor would have nothing to do with any of this. If I was a doctor and one of my patients cured their cancer with a natural oil, I would be extremely interested. Yet, my doctor would not even talk about what had transpired with the use of this oil, so I felt the behavior of the receptionist and my doctor towards this issue was very strange indeed.

After the disappointing experience in my doctor's office, I began to supply oil to others for topical use. In a short time, it became obvious that this oil had amazing healing powers and was an effective treatment for a vast number of skin conditions and other medical problems. A few months later, I started providing oil to treat internal conditions like cancer, multiple sclerosis, chronic pain and just about every other malady you can imagine.

When the use of this oil comes into play in the treatment of a patient, the rulebook goes out the window. Conditions deemed hopeless were now controllable and in many cases curable with the use of nothing other than the oil. From my experience, this substance can replace practically all pharmaceuticals. Anyone who is concerned about what the medical system provides will be relieved to know that they no longer have to ingest the poisons and chemicals doctors supply to treat their medical problems. Now there is a perfectly safe, natural, non-addictive medication that you can grow and produce yourself, so who needs Big Pharma and medicine which doesn't work?

In 2003, I started a campaign to bring the truth about the hemp plant's medicinal effectiveness to those who were in authority. I sent large information packages and a proposal to manufacture this medication by registered mail to government officials, the Canadian Cancer Society, the UN, science and health TV shows etc. but no one expressed an interest. When I started sending all this information out, I really believed at the time that they would welcome a medication which was effective and caused no harm. Instead, to my horror, I found that our system really did not want an effective cure or control for anything. The rich elite who control our governments are making too much money off our illnesses, so to them allowing the public to have the free medicinal use of hemp would be out of the question. It was a hard pill for me to swallow but, sadly, that is the way our world is being run. The health of the public means nothing to them and profit margins are their only concern.

Due to my activities, I was raided by the Royal Canadian Mounted police in 2003, 2005, and 2006. Even though I had informed the RCMP about what I was doing and how many people the oil was helping, they continued on with their interference. It seemed that the police were more than happy to take part in the crime of keeping this medication from those in need. Even though they themselves and their loved ones are suffering at the hands of the same medical system, which we the public are exposed to, as well.

Doctors in the local area were aware of what this oil was doing and even though many had seen the wonderful medicinal effect the oil had on their own patients, none would come forward. It seems they realized the effect such a medicine would have on their profession. So, to protect their incomes and maintain the status they enjoyed, it would be in their best interest to ignore hemp. The way I look at it, if a doctor will not prescribe the most medicinal plant on Earth, they are not doctors. Instead, they are bought and paid for drug dealers who are working for the pharmaceutical industry.

I really don't think it can be said that doctors even have an excuse for what they have been doing. If you asked a 10-year-old if poison and chemicals are good for them, instantly they would reply no. Now ask your doctor the same question and they will tell you these dangerous substances are necessary to treat your condition effectively. Whose leg do these guys think they are pulling? According to them, chemicals and poison are now good for you, so while we're at it, we might as well start believing that black is white.

The medical system we endure today is a complete fraud and if you are suffering from a medical problem, likely you would receive better treatment if you went to someone with a bone through their nose instead of your trusted physician. That is the state our medical system is in today and the only medical professionals I put any trust in are the surgeons. Yet, even their abilities should be looked into carefully, before you allow them to proceed.

When I was raided in 2003 and 2006, charges were not laid but in 2005, I was charged with possession, trafficking and cultivation. When I entered the court system, I knew what I was doing did not belong in a court of law. I had already been to all the right people and even had newspaper articles done, detailing my activities long before I was ever charged. I had been open and honest in all respects about this issue and if the legal system had not been so corrupted themselves, this case would have been thrown right back in the government's face. Sadly, this did not take place. Instead, the legal system decided to proceed with their goal of trying to make me look like a criminal in the eyes of the public.

I went through a Charter challenge under the Charter of Rights and Freedoms in Canada and a Supreme Court of Nova Scotia trial over this issue. After seeing how all these legal eagles practice their profession, I can only report that our legal system is just as corrupted as the government who controls them. The judge and the lawyers all knew what I was telling them was true, but if they did the right thing, it would upset the status quo. So the judge in all his wisdom would not allow the patients who had used the oil to testify.

I sat in that courtroom and watched this judge and these lawyers destroy any semblance of justice that I ever thought existed in Canada. In the end, the only way they could get a conviction was to tamper with the jury and the crown prosecutor did not hesitate to do so. Even though the judge was later informed about what had transpired, he protected the crown prosecutor by sweeping it all under the rug.

Everything I had believed about my own country went down the drain and I realized all these people I had dealt with were simply evil to the core. Was there anything that those who were put in positions of public trust would not do for a paycheck or kickback? From what I had seen, it appeared that these individuals were quite capable of anything, no matter how low and disgusting it may be. They had broken every rule in the book to see that I was found guilty and in the end even the jury which should have found me innocent, allowed them to have their way. In the early stages of my case, a publication ban had been put in place so the general public had no idea what was truly going on. Due to this ban, which was imposed without my consent, I can only wonder what would have happened if the public had been better informed about what was actually taking place.

At my sentencing on February 8, 2008, it was obvious the legal system was a bit uncomfortable with what they had done. Before we entered the courtroom that day, everyone was put through a metal detector. Never before had I ever heard of metal detectors being used at the Amherst courthouse, so it seems these legal types may have been in fear of their lives. A good number of people had showed up that day for my sentencing and it wasn't hard to tell whose side they were on. During my trial, the judge had refused to allow the patients who used this medication to give their testimony. In addition, he also did not seem to feel compelled to hear testimony from the doctors I had called into court and would not allow the scientific evidence to be introduced. When the judge began my sentencing, he stated that under different circumstances I would be winning awards for my work and that in his 34 years in the legal system, he had never seen a case like this. There was no criminal intent.

He then stated the scientific evidence does exist to back up everything I was saying and that I have treated many patients who also back my position. The statements the judge had just made were never proven in court because he had not allowed any of this evidence to be introduced. Therefore, it was obvious to all who were present that he had exposed the fact he did indeed have prior knowledge. If this were really so, then why had they put me through this idiotic court case, instead of doing what was right in the first place?

After seeing the levels of deception to which they would stoop in their never-ending quest to keep the public misinformed, I had reached the point that I strongly suspected none of them were capable of facing the grim reality of what was truly going on, so it really was a surprise to me when this judge came out with the truth. I suppose, in the position he was in he had no choice other than to bring out the facts, because there were many people present in the courtroom that day, who were well aware of the truth. I was facing a possible sentence of twelve years in prison for the crime of helping my fellow man, but the sentence I was to receive was left to the judge's own discretion. I was given a 2,000-dollar fine and a gun restriction, although no guns were ever found during the raids conducted on my property, and I was not even put on probation. Instead of everyone being overjoyed that finally we had a medicine which could really help the human race, it was ignored as if nothing had happened.

After getting this court case over with, I started to look for a country where I might go to live that was run a bit more honestly. I was very depressed over my government's behavior but that didn't stop people from becoming sick and the patients kept coming. I never had a problem with trying to help others but how was I to continue under these circumstances? As time went on, many police officers began to support my activities and some were even sending patients my way for treatment. By all appearances, it seemed that many were starting to wake up and I thought that finally our system was coming to its senses. Whenever I had the opportunity, I did interviews and seminars on this subject and now word was really spreading rapidly. Just because our government was perfectly happy to see us slaughtered was no reason for me to behave in the same manner, so I could do little else but continue on the same path, I had been traveling.

In 2009, Jindrich Bayer invited me to do a speaking tour in the Czech Republic and I asked Jack if he was interested in taking part. He jumped at the opportunity, but about two weeks before the tour was to begin, Jack collapsed from the heart attack. When this occurred, I almost cancelled the tour, but I swear I could hear Jack's voice besieging me to carry on. Dr. Lumir Hanus, one of the greatest hemp researchers on the planet was scheduled to take part, so we decided the tour must go on. I spent about three weeks in the Czech Republic and the tour was a great success with the public. Even though government took little interest, there was no question that we had managed to get our message to the people, so I considered the tour to be time well spent.

When I returned to Canada, I had a lot of catching up to do with the patients, but by November 20, I had taken care of it all and I was ready to leave for the Cannabis Cup in Amsterdam. Another Canadian named Scot

Cullins, who had also treated a good number of patients with this medication came to Amsterdam with me and we had a very good time together. At the cup, I put on a seminar about this subject and the last day of the event I was to be crowned Freedom Fighter of the Year.

The day before I was to be crowned, I received word from Canada that once again my property had been raided by the RCMP. The police were telling the news media that they had found restricted weapons, booby traps and 70 pounds of pot on my property. Of course, I knew none of what the police were stating was true, so it was obvious to me the RCMP were trying to pull one of their famous frame-ups and in reality this police force has an extensive history of doing just that.

By using the news media to tell the public that booby traps and restricted weapons, plus seventy pounds of pot was found on my property, that sent the message I was a very dangerous person. If the RCMP could make the public believe all this, it would help to discredit what I was doing and also make it much easier for them to lock me away. For quite some time, I had been a very big thorn in the Canadian government's backside over this issue. Since I was out of the country when the raid occurred, I tend to believe that the government used this opportunity to have the police try to set me up.

I don't think the Canadian government realized how much notoriety this subject was receiving and I believe this raid was staged to keep me from returning. If this really was their aim, it was a success. Knowing what I do about the Canadian legal system, a man would have to be a lunatic to even think about going back to all that corruption. I knew if I returned that I would have to face these bogus charges, but what bothered me most was, I would be locked up without the medication I require. If I were to go back and allow this to happen, it would be little more than suicide on my part. I needed time for public opinion to swing more in my favor and I would have to write a book to expose what really had gone on, so people would become aware. Since I didn't see any other option, I decided to remain in exile and finish the battle from Europe. The Canadian government branded me as a criminal. Now, with a bit of time and some effort, I am going to show the public who the real criminals are.

Our world is controlled by the rich banking elite who go by names like Rothschild, Rockefeller, Warburg, Carnegie etc. They are the ones who own the news media, drug companies, oil companies and almost everything else. In addition, they happen to be the ones who control our governments and their policies. We are told that we live in countries, but in reality we exist in corporations that look at the human race no differently than farm animals. Our governments do not represent the best interests of their people. All the major parties in politics are under the thumb of big money interests. When these parties come to power, we often question why they did not keep their election promises.

Why this takes place is quite simple. How could we expect them to keep their word, when those who are their real masters want otherwise? The mega rich seem to look at us all as if we were their property. If we try to put up a struggle against their manipulation, in many cases, their police and legal systems are sent to deal with us, at other times the person who is causing the controversy simply disappears. The public do not like to dwell on events of this nature, but they do happen and we all know that greed is the main cause.

If those who have all the wealth and power were running our planet properly, we would have little to complain about. Yet, this is hardly the case. In the last hundred years, they have done more damage to this earth than in all human history combined. Just look at the recent oil spill in the Gulf of Mexico and tell me if you think this disaster could have been avoided. If we were free to grow hemp to help fulfill our energy needs, there would be no reason to continue drilling for oil. We all know that the use of fossil fuels is poisoning our planet. So why do we allow this to go on when we could be using earth-friendly fuels like ethanol produced from hemp?

Now I would like to mention one of the worst catastrophes in human history, the Fukushima nuclear power plant disaster. When this event occurred, I was horrified. In the past, I had looked into the dangers involved in harnessing the power of the atom. If I had been living in Japan when this disaster took place, I would have been looking for a way to get off the island as quickly as possible. In fact, I would not be surprised in the end that everyone will have to evacuate the island of Japan to get away from all the radiation emanating from the destroyed reactors. It's not only the people of Japan who are at risk, although they certainly are the ones in the greatest danger, now we are all standing in the path of this invisible monster. In the future, its effects will cause untold suffering and death, unless we are allowed to use hemp oil to protect our bodies.

Dealing with patients in the past, I have seen radiation burns so bad that the patients' chest looked like it was made from red leather. After treatment with the oil, the damage just disappeared, leaving healthy pink skin. If the oil can do this for a patient that has been damaged by radiation in a hospital, I see no reason it would not do the same for those of us who are now being exposed to the radiation escaping from Japan.

The use of nuclear energy presents a huge danger to the public and it comes with many problems that are impossible to solve. For instance, what are they going to do with the spent fuel rods, after they are removed from the reactors? There is no safe way to store such material and no matter what we do, the human race will always be in jeopardy from exposure. The energy companies try to tell us we cannot do without this form of energy to supply our needs, but I doubt that very much. The same ethanol we could use to power our cars can also be used to run our power generating systems. In reality, there is no rational excuse for us to allow these big money concerns to carry on with the destruction they are bringing to our world. As humans, we have the right to choose our destiny and no longer will we bow down to the wishes of corrupted governments or profit-oriented monsters.

This is our world and we humans have the right to live in good health and freedom no matter how the big money interests want to look at it, their days of controlling us are over. We are the human race and we will do whatever is necessary to ensure our survival. So even the wealthiest among us, had better begin to learn the error of their ways, or they could indeed face consequences of a horrifying nature. The dark days of our enslavement to big money are just about at an end and soon we will all find the better world we are seeking. It's up to us to do what needs to be done and if you are unwilling to do so, then who on god's green earth will?

Everything Jack showed us in "The Emperor Wears No Clothes" is based in fact and in reality, he was quite right when he stated that hemp holds the key to our future. Now that the true medicinal value of this plant is becoming widely known, we would have to be insane to allow things to carry on the way they have been. To me, there is no real law which prevents us from growing and using the cannabis hemp plant in whatever way we like, nor has such a law ever existed.

When laws are put in place, they are supposed to be based on the principle that what is being outlawed is causing harm. Hemp does not cause harm and who in their right mind would outlaw what was historically recognized to be the most medicinal plant on earth? These absurd laws are founded in corruption and nothing more, so why should we be expected to adhere to them? Real laws cannot be enacted in this manner and now it's time to let those who represent us know we will no longer be dictated to. No one ever had the right to outlaw the use of this plant, no matter what their purpose and for us to continue to ignore its medical virtues is incomprehensible.

The hemp plant was put on this earth for us all to use freely for food, fiber, medicine, energy and a multitude of other applications. At last count, over 50,000 different things can be produced from this amazing plant. When these unlawful restrictions are removed, it will put people back on the land where they belong. Once again, they will get in touch with nature and become much more self-sufficient. Millions of jobs would then be there for the taking in earth-friendly hemp-based industries and, in a short time, we could have a hemp-based economy.

Can you not see the world that Jack Herer and I envision and does it not make much more sense than the way our world is being managed today? If you want your children to have a future, the time to act is now, for tomorrow may be too late. As in all things, there is a point of no return and our earth can only endure so much before it reaches a state where it cannot support human life as we know it.

If we grow hemp on a grand scale, this plant can help bring about the necessary changes and give our planet and all living things a badly needed second chance. So, in the interest of self-preservation, I implore you to join with me in doing what is rational. We have the power to transform this world into the paradise it should be instead of the hell it has become and it is our duty to coming generations for us to fulfill this role.

I have a great deal of hope for the human race and once we become more enlightened, I think we could finally become the brotherhood of man. Now that the path we must take is clear, there is no reason to hesitate. We must bring about a new way of living, as peacefully and quickly as possible. The time of our redemption is at hand and hemp is the plant which will make it all possible. We are a species that knows how to overcome adversity and indeed, we must now take on the responsibility of getting our world back on the right track.

Until this comes to pass, I wish you all the best that life has to offer. We all have the right to be healthy and happy and in a short span of time, we should be able to achieve this goal. So get off your chesterfields and join the hemp revolution, we are going to make this world take notice and no matter who or what stands in our path, we will succeed. Long live the memory of Jack Herer and let us never forget the cause, for which he fought in such a magnificent manner. Jack, you are the man and now, in your absence, we will do our best to follow the example you have set.

CHAPTER 9

FIGHTING THE DAMAGE CAUSED
BY RADIATION

After the horrible earthquake in Japan that has caused all this damage to many of the nuclear reactors that are operating in that country, radiation is now spreading worldwide. With high levels of radiation being released into the atmosphere on a continuous basis, it will have a devastating effect on the lives of most living creatures. Yet, once again, if used properly, high quality hemp oil can provide a solution that will be of great help to mankind in alleviating this situation.

For years, I have been telling the public that every man woman and child on this earth should be taking small doses of this oil every day to maintain good health. With all the radiation that is now entering our atmosphere, it is basically urgent that we now all start ingesting this oil as soon as possible, to undo the damage this radiation will cause. Through my experience with the use of this oil, I have found that there is nothing more effective or more harmless, which can reduce the damage caused by radiation.

I have seen patients who suffered from cancer, which were badly damaged by the effects of radiation treatments that were able to eliminate the damage this so-called medical treatment had caused. Some patients who have come to me that had taken radiation, were burned and poisoned so badly by its effects that in the beginning, I really did not believe anything could undo this type of harm. After ingesting the oil treatment, their skin went back to its normal healthy state and the radiation burns disappeared completely. If the oil can do this for someone who has been severely damaged by the medical system, would its use not also be effective to combat the effects of the radiation, now emanating from Japan?

There are thousands of reasons as to why the medicinal use of the cannabis plant should never have been restricted in the first place. Now, with the menace that all this escaping radiation presents, we would have to be insane to turn our backs on the use of hemp extracts to help us all deal with this situation. I truly feel sorry for the misery the people of Japan are now going through and if nothing can be done to stop the radiation from escaping, they may lose their homeland entirely.

Don't be fooled by government double talk regarding this issue, radiation is an invisible but dangerous threat to the well-being of us all and only a complete fool would try to say otherwise. The wondrous medicinal effects of properly produced oil from the cannabis hemp plant are finally being recognized once more worldwide.

Fighting the effects of radiation is just one more reason we must begin to start growing this plant again on a grand scale and it is time that we all told our governments that we have had enough of their nonsense. Our very lives and the lives of coming generations, plus the well-being of many other species are at stake and it is now up to us to determine what kind of future humanity is to have.

CHAPTER 10

CAUSE AND EFFECT

From 2003 onward when I first started supplying this medication produced from the cannabis hemp plant, its use has exploded worldwide and continues to be recognized more and more every day by those who are sick and suffering everywhere. But our trusted medical and political systems thus far have refused to react to our needs as they should and this is truly a crime against us all.

One of the main excuses we often hear governments use is that the United Nations has regulations in place, which keep this plant's medicinal use prohibited. If there really were a sensible reason as to why the UN put these regulations in place, we would have little to complain about. But judging from the truth of the matter, it seems obvious to me that the restrictions which the UN initiated were certainly not put in force to ease human suffering or help us in any way.

The UN is controlled by Big Money concerns and in reality has done little or nothing to really help the advancement of the human race. So, as far as I'm concerned, if those who represent us were truly working on our behalf, they would no longer allow organizations such as the United Nations to continue to perpetrate these crimes against humanity. I am a firm believer in law and order, but when the public is subjected to regulations such as this, which are obviously doing so much harm, I think it's just about time the citizens of all countries got together and demanded that governments begin to react to their needs.

At present, most who are using the essential oil of this plant to heal themselves are classified as criminals due to the corrupted laws, which have been put in place to restrict this plant's medicinal use. Does it seem sensible to you that we have laws in effect which prevents us from having the right to heal ourselves with a natural, harmless, non-addictive oil produced from the hemp plant?

I don't know about you, but to me this all reads much like a script which was written for a bad science fiction movie and since in reality this has all taken place, it appears that we are living in little more than the Twilight Zone? How could a situation like this have ever occurred and why are we all not doing more to put an end to this travesty? Put simply, our world is being run by overly rich and powerful individuals who wish to dominate our existence, while generating huge profits for themselves and their investors.

Decades ago, their money and influence corrupted governments almost everywhere into having this wonderful plant outlawed without just cause. They were able to accomplish all this by renaming cannabis hemp marijuana, which is simply one of hundreds of slang terms that I consider to be derogatory which are used worldwide to describe this plant. For the most part, back when all this came about, the public had no idea what marijuana even was and they had no knowledge that what their trusted governments were really outlawing was indeed a plant, which had been used in medicine with good effect for thousands of years. This is why I can openly state that there has never been a real law against this plant's growing and use. The restrictions we currently have in place are all based in corruption, which was spawned by the wealthy elite to achieve their aims.

There is not now nor has there ever been any rational reason as to why this plant's medicinal use was ever restricted. It was greed and the lust for more power by those who are the richest among us that has brought this all about. Mankind has been suffering at the hands of these sick-minded individuals for far too long and I for one feel it's just about time that we all endeavor to free ourselves from their manipulation. Not only have they been tampering with our health by denying this medicine's use, which has brought about the suffering and death of countless numbers. We also have to look at the damage those with vast amounts of money and resources have done to our earth.

Two glaring examples of the horrible consequences these uncaring individuals have caused would be the Gulf oil spill and the Fukushima nuclear disaster, both of which should never have happened, since there are much more sensible and harmless ways to solve our energy requirements. Unfortunately, the list of horrific events which the twisted thinking of the mega rich have caused is almost endless. Everywhere, it seems, death and destruction is the order of the day and the inhumanity of those who are causing all this appears to have no bounds.

Should we all just stand by doing nothing, while innocent people are slaughtered in vast numbers all over the globe and our world is being torn asunder right before our very eyes? If so, then we should all get out our picks and shovels and begin digging our own graves because in the near future we will likely have a great need for them. When you awaken to the reality of what is truly happening, it seems inconceivable and it's enough to make any sensible person scream, "Stop the world and let me off." Surely by this time the human race is coming to realize that something must be done and the time to do it is now, if we are to indeed provide ourselves and our loved ones with a decent future. To avoid the destruction of our earth and the different forms of life it supports, we must all begin to think a bit more rationally. Since the hemp plant can furnish us with just about everything we need to sustain our existence, I see no option other than to grow this plant freely everywhere and use it in every possible way.

If we are truly serious about detoxifying this earth and saving ourselves, there is nothing else on this planet which can perform this task other than the cannabis hemp plant. Food, fuel, medicine and just about everything else we use in our day-to-day lives can be manufactured from hemp. Whatever we are now producing from petroleum can also be manufactured from cannabis hemp in a much more earth-friendly and sustainable manner. So in the future there should be no reason to continue fighting these senseless wars over petroleum and other resources when there are much more sensible ways to deal with our energy problems.

We do not need more oil wells and petroleum or nuclear energy. We need more cannabis hemp and people with the backbone to make it so. Truly, it can only be said that our governments are not representing the best interests of their people by allowing this plant's growing and use to remain restricted. In truth, it has become more than obvious that most governments are behaving in a criminal fashion towards our overall health and well-being. This is not the role our elected officials are supposed to be playing, and if they are unwilling to represent us honestly, then in reality what right do they have to call themselves our governments?

My good friend Max Igan has devised a very simple method in which we should be able to have governments respond to the needs of their citizens. If they refuse to comply with the will of the people, they are then in breach of trust and have proven themselves to be unworthy of representing us. Max is proposing that we present governments with a People's Mandate and I think what he has in mind could have a very beneficial effect upon our future. I will not try to go any deeper into this subject because Max is here today to explain the concept himself. So when he gives his lecture, please listen carefully and I think you will agree that what he is saying just makes good sense.

Now I will get back to a subject in which I have a bit more expertise. The use of the term drugs is used in the field of medicine and it is also used on the street to describe dangerous substances that people commonly use to become intoxicated from their effects. The use of most of these substances obviously does present a danger because many are addictive and deadly and there is no question that this is so. Since cannabis hemp is neither addictive nor dangerous, why are so many people calling it a drug? To me, cannabis is simply a medicine that can be used with good effect, either recreationally or otherwise. Even the smoking aspect of this plant has medicinal benefits but the real medical miracles that cannabis can provide will only be found in the proper use of essential oils produced from the buds of strong medicinal strains.

What do we perceive as being medicine and what do we base our perceptions on? The Hippocratic Oath exposes the way medicine should be practiced, yet for the most part doctors do not follow their own oath. The wording of this oath states, "First do no harm." But medical professionals use chemicals, poisons, radiation and things such as CT scans, which expose their patients to even more radiation on a regular basis. Could what doctors have been doing actually be called the practice of medicine? At the present time, judging by the methods they employ to treat their patients, it certainly does not sound that way to me. In reality, history shows us that this profession has always taken a rather strange approach to the art of healing, which for some reason seems to be largely forgotten today, but I do think it bares reminder.

Not so long ago, doctors often employed the use of such things as bloodletting and mercury to treat the sick and suffering and this type of thing went on for an enormous length of time. Today we all know the effects of such so-called treatments and it only makes one wonder why doctors in years gone by would employ their use for such a long period of time? How many deaths would one have to witness before they would finally realize that the treatments themselves, which they had provided, were probably responsible for the patient's demise? With this in mind, it becomes quite clear that even way back then doctors were very good at rejecting the simple truth, which was starring them in the face every time one of their so-called treatments killed someone.

Sadly for us all, doctors of today are little different. If the patient dies, it is never their fault. The medical condition they suffered from caused them to pass on or God was calling them home. This is the type of non-sense grieving families and friends are told by their trusted physicians and clergymen. Yet, sadly, one only has to look at the substances and treatments, which the medical system currently employs to learn the truth about such deaths. Chemicals, poison, and radiation do not heal and are things that should be avoided if we wish those who are ill to survive. Even most ten-year-old children know this to be true. So why do our trusted doctors seem unable to accept what even a young child can understand?

In reality, it's all about the money, folks, and in truth our governments and medical systems have proven that they have no concern at all for our health and well-being. They are using our health care systems to feed the greed of the rich and powerful, which they serve. Since this is obviously what has been taking place, one can only surmise that they are all working in league with the devil and they could care less about how many of us are killed needlessly, as long as they themselves are prospering.

Why would our trusted political and medical systems want to use natural, harmless, and effective medications produced from the hemp plant to help the sick and suffering when so much revenue can be generated for their rich masters by continuing to harm the public with chemicals and poisons? There are no big profits to be found in providing natural medications that really do heal, for then there would be little return business to keep the coffers of drug companies overflowing. It's best for the bottom line of these big drug firms if they can continue to have us use their products, which will keep us all sick and suffering, while remaining at their mercy.

I don't know how any logical person could consider what we are being subjected to by our doctors as being medicine. Often we are told that doctors must follow regulations and only use medications and treatments which are approved, but this is just simply a very lame excuse that has been used far too often for what is currently taking place. A doctor's first concern must be the health and well-being of their patients. If one is truly to call themselves a doctor, they would have to ensure that their patients received the safest and most sensible medications or treatments available. If they were to do so, they would then be following their own Hippocratic Oath and they would also need to supply extracts produced from hemp and other harmless medicinal plants to fulfill that oath. Since what I'm describing is obviously true, but still our medical systems refuse to use cannabis and other healing medicinal plants properly, could someone please tell me why we allow this to continue?

I think you have to admit that when an ordinary person can take a rice cooker, some solvent and hemp bud, then produce a medicine themselves that is far superior to anything the medical system offers, then indeed it could only be said that we have little or no medical systems at all. Would what is going on become more apparent to the masses if we simply started calling what they are doing to us by its proper term, which would be the programmed demolition of our bodies and health? I for one refuse to allow those in white coats to do such things to me and every day more and more individuals are coming to feel the same. Enough with all the false statements and lies, we are now aware of what doctors have been doing to us and with the use of hemp and other harmless natural healing substances, in a short time we can provide ourselves with medicines which really do work.

As an added bonus, often we will no longer even be compelled to seek the advice of a doctor, for in most cases there will be little need to do so. Now with the proper use of hemp extracts, most patients can become their own physicians and heal themselves in a harmless natural manner. If any of us were to become afflicted with a serious medical condition, it's far better at present to rely on medications we can produce ourselves. Medications which we are aware have been proven to work. Instead of putting our faith in a medical system we know to be badly flawed due to greed and corruption. Our bodies belong to us and if we choose to treat ourselves with harmless natural medications, who has the right to say this is not allowed? As far as I'm concerned, the show is over for Big Pharma along with those in control of these companies and all those misguided individuals who have been supporting them.

Now we have a sensible answer to most of our health problems and no power on this earth is going to keep it from us. Why should we obey their corrupted laws, rules and regulations in regards to the medicinal use of cannabis hemp? If you or someone you care about is in need of treatment, acquire or grow the proper material to produce this medication, it can mean the difference between life and death. Then let your governments know that you are no longer willing to abide by their absurd laws regarding this plant's medicinal restrictions.

Historically, cannabis hemp produced man's oldest known and safest medications. Also it was noted that cannabis is non-addictive and not one death has ever been attributed to its medicinal use. What other medications, which are currently employed by our doctors, can even make such a claim? Practically every so-called medicinal substance we are provided with is known to do some harm to the body and often their effects can be very deadly. Even simple off-the-shelf items like aspirin and other seemingly harmless so-called medicinal substances, which are supplied by the big drug firms, are causing tens of thousands of deaths each year worldwide. Thousands of years before the time of Jesus, hemp was being employed for medicinal purposes and I strongly suspect that Christ himself made good use of its healing virtues.

If the greatest healers in history did not hesitate to employ cannabis hemp to aid in their patients' recoveries, why do we allow its use to be prohibited today? Extracts produced from this plant have already proven themselves to be effective in curing or controlling practically every human malady, and in all honesty I cannot name a disease, upon which this wonder of nature is not of benefit in treating. Therefore, I cannot help but feel that there is no longer a need for any further controversy over this subject. If this plant and the oil it produces cannot be considered medicine, then what else on this earth could be?

What I am saying has been proven countless times by vast numbers of people worldwide. Just look at the information and testimonials available on the Internet. If all this were not true, then why would so many people now be coming forward? Since our trusted news media is controlled by the same individuals and their friends, who wish to keep this plant's use restricted, today the only place the truth can be found is on the internet and that truth is literally screaming that something must be done.

The medical system keeps telling us that cannabis needs more study before its medicinal use can be recognized. What they are stating is only a stalling tactic, which the rich and powerful have been employing for years to maintain control. To me, listening to such nonsense is becoming rather tiresome and I think by now that it should be having about the same effect on all of us. Have we not already listened to enough of this unsubstantiated double talk? And how many people have to die needlessly before all this type of misleading rhetoric comes to an end? Not everyone will fail to remember those who are responsible for this situation and it is the continuing manipulation of these individuals that is causing so many at present to suffer.

I don't care how you look at it, those who are responsible for these deeds are committing outright murder, no matter if they are unwilling to admit it to themselves or not. Nevertheless, when they expose us to chemicals and poisons disguised as medicine, then restrict us from the use of a natural harmless medicinal substance, which can save our lives, this is called genocide. How could depriving vast numbers of those who are suffering, from the use of a natural medication they require to heal properly be looked at in any other way? Yet, individuals who blindly support the restriction of this plant's medicinal use go on uttering the same lame-brained excuses without even considering the harm and devastation these bogus statements are causing to those who are actually sick and suffering.

If those with limited intelligence choose to support the use of what the medical system supplies today, it is their right. But do not think for a second that those among us with a brain that still functions will feel compelled to do the same. If you wish to allow yourself to be harmed, or even killed by drugs and treatments employed by our current medical systems, then by all means allow the doctors to have their way with you. But as for those of us with reasoning abilities, we will take a much more sensible approach to healing ourselves.

I know these are strong statements to be coming from someone such as myself. But they are all based in fact. If they were not, what I have been saying publicly would have been debunked by medical professionals a long time ago. The reason they have avoided trying to do so is simple. They cannot disprove a thing I have stated and they know it, but I can expose what they have been doing to the public in the blink of an eye.

To those of you who are not familiar with this subject, you may find my attitude towards politicians and the medical system etc. to be somewhat extreme. But for the past decade, I have been doing everything in my power to bring this to the attention of physicians and those who are supposed to represent our needs in government circles, but as yet my efforts have been futile. There is as yet no law against being misinformed, or ignorant about a subject. But when the actions of those in political and medical circles show a total disregard for reality and are causing hundreds of millions of needless deaths every year, I think that it's time for us all to begin to place our trust elsewhere.

It really makes one wonder what is wrong with our society, when countless doctors have watched their own patients heal themselves with the use of this natural substance and yet still they remain quiet. I have also witnessed those involved in politics and the legal profession, who were well aware of this medication's effectiveness refuse to lift a finger. Could these really be considered individuals, in which we are supposed to put our trust?

Watching well-educated and supposedly intelligent people who are in positions of authority turn their backs on such a simple truth for this length of time can be somewhat frustrating. For years now, these individuals have expressed no interest, so I am no longer willing to waste my time, trying to convince those in political and medical circles to act. Since everyone in authority I have come into contact with thus far have made it clear that they are behaving in a criminal fashion towards those they are supposed to serve, I could care less now about what they think or say.

My mission is simply to provide the truth to everyone possible, so together we can affect change and through our website and the information we distribute, now almost everyone can produce their own medicine to heal themselves. I openly challenge any doctor to appear with me before a live audience, or better yet, why don't we do this right over national television stations? Let's see whose statements the viewing audience will accept about what is medicine and what is not. In addition, I would like the medical system to show us any medication commonly in use for any condition that would be more harmless or effective to ease a patients suffering than properly produced hemp oil. Unfortunately, I doubt very strongly that such an event will ever occur, for if it did, the whole medical system would be exposed and this is not something that the powers that be would like to see take place before the general public.

High-grade cannabis extracts are substances which all medications deemed fit for human consumption should be measured against. Why do drug companies use placebos in their so-called studies to determine what they intend to sell the public is safe and effective in solving their medical issues? If those in charge of drug companies really wanted to know the truth about the medications they are trying to sell and shove down our throats. Why are the concoctions they produce not measured against hemp extracts to determine how safe and effective they really are? The reason that they do not do this is quite clear, since it would prove the substances they manufacture and distribute do present a danger to the public and, when compared with what nature can provide, are much less medicinally active and safe.

Therefore, it begs the question as to why any highly trained medical professional would try to use these chemicals and poisons and expect them to help someone regain their health. Practically everything pharmaceutical companies tell us about the medical virtues of their products is a hoax that has been perpetrated against us by both drug companies and the FDA to instill confidence in that which they wish the public to use as medicines. To those who seem to lack any moral responsibility for what they are doing, this all might be looked at as just being good business. But every day, for many of us, their lies and manipulation can cause untold suffering and put vast numbers of those who could have been healed in an early grave.

I am not just some guy, who is telling you all this so I can mislead you and fill my pockets. If you'd seen how badly my bank account has been overdrawn for the last few years, no doubt this would be all the proof you need. When I started doing all this, my aim was simply to help the human race by providing them with medicine and information that can ease their suffering and save their lives. We were able to accomplish this by putting all the information needed to produce this medicine yourself and how to use it properly up on our website at www.phoenixtears.ca.

Then Christian Laurette, a very talented young man from Amherst, Nova Scotia, produced and released our documentary "Run From the Cure" in early 2008. By that time, I had supplied this oil to countless individuals with cancer and many other types of medical problems. The effectiveness of this oil in the treatment of practically all medical difficulties was truly astounding. But to prevent the truth from becoming known, the Canadian government has given me a criminal record and they have done everything short of physically harming me to prevent my message of hope from reaching the masses.

We had also published my book "The Rick Simpson Story", and at present it is available at www.simpsonramadur.com. Even though my book has been available for the last few years and the facts have been laid bare for all to see, still as yet nothing has been done. If you want to learn the ugly truth about the world in which we live, you will find it between the covers of this book. After reading it, I'm sure you will feel the same disgust that I do for those who have caused all this to take place. That is why I am here in Europe, hoping to find a country, which is run a bit more honestly, in which this life-saving medication can be openly produced.

Many who attend the events, at which I appear, are trying to acquire some oil to help themselves or a loved one. But sadly, due to the laws which still exist, I have very few contacts in Europe, who can supply the proper material needed to produce this substance. So please do not vent your anger on me, because I cannot supply the medication, which you require. I am not among those who are trying to deny its use. If you are looking to blame someone, look no further than your trusted governments, for they were the ones who put these so-called laws in place.

Back in Canada, I knew many individuals that were growing the right strains required to produce this medication properly on a fairly large scale. Still, due to all the demand for this substance, in a very short time I would usually exhaust their supply. But over here in Europe, I cannot speak the different languages and I don't have the contacts to even supply my own needs, on a steady basis. Plus, many growers in Europe do not as yet grow the most potent and sedative indica or indica dominant strains that I recommend. These absurd laws, which are currently in place, are keeping the price of good medicinal hemp bud very high and even if patients can find the needed material, often they cannot afford to purchase it. If this plant were allowed to be grown properly without interference from governments and police, you could buy a kilo of high-grade medicinal bud for practically nothing to solve your medical issues.

I am more than willing to prove everything I'm saying. All I need is a government somewhere that will give me the OK. If there is a country anywhere, which is willing to turn me loose and let me show them what this plant can do, in no time they will have more proof than they will know what to do with. I have been traveling now for three years and I can tell you from personal experience that living out of a suitcase for an extended period of time is not an experience, which one enjoys. I feel now that my time could be better spent staying in one place for a while, so I can get on with my research and begin taking the medication I require on a more regular basis. If there is an honest government out there that really has the best interests of their people at heart, please contact me and I'm sure, we can work something out. The truth in what I'm saying is plastered all over the internet and there is no shortage of testimonials or scientific evidence to back up everything that this amazing medication can do for the human race.

Since the medicinal use of cannabis has now been decriminalized in so many countries, surely there is some place, which would welcome my expertise in the production of this medication. If we worked together, it would not only help your people, but in the end, such a country would be setting an example for the rest of the world to follow. I am not looking for a revolution. My only goal is to see change and to accomplish this, we must go about it in the proper manner.

Should we seek retribution? No, we should not. I do not want to hear about anyone carrying out acts of violence against their doctors and elected officials. After all, they are no different than most of us and they too were fed the same unfounded propaganda about this plant, which we were.

Unlike many of us, sadly it seems that most of these individuals are unable to come to terms with the simple truth, which is now before them and are only capable of regurgitating the falsehoods they were told in the past. But even though those in positions of authority have been more than a bit slow to act in doing anything positive about this situation, I still feel that no harm should be directed towards them. I also do not wish to see violence carried out against the rich elite, who have been giving the human race so much grief. But to put a stop to their activities, I do feel that they must be dealt with in a sensible manner.

The fortunes these mega rich individuals and families have amassed is in reality, the proceeds from the crimes that they have committed against us all. When criminals are caught, the funds they have stolen are confiscated and returned to their victims. Since it is a well-known fact how many mega rich families like the Rothschilds and Rockefellers etc. came by their fortunes, should we not take what they have stolen from us back and put these resources in the hands of individuals, who will do something good for this world?

Instead of regulating and taxing cannabis, as some so-called hemp activists have suggested, why do we simply not get together and bring those who have been harming us to justice? I think this could be accomplished if we were to bring these individuals into a real common law court, then confront them with all the evidence of their crimes, until they admit their guilt, after which they should be stripped of their money and power so they can do no further damage.

Since the rich elite have never been subjected to the hard work that many of us have, I doubt that most of them could even function well in the real world. It may be too generous on my part, but after admitting their guilt, I feel that they should be set free and left with enough so they can live out of the rest of their lives in at least some comfort. In truth, these individuals have committed many sinister deeds and there is no question that their thinking and reasoning is of a psychopathic nature. But still, I cannot help but look at them all as simply being people who are suffering with mental issues and I'm sure the oil would help many of them think a bit more clearly.

What I am suggesting may sound irrational to some, but what other sensible solution is there to the dilemma, which we currently face? Should we just stand by and watch the rich elite finish destroying our planet? Or be content to see our governments continue to misrepresent our needs and deny us from the right to use this God-given plant to heal ourselves? I can only hope that we will not allow this to take place.

All we have to do is unite and governments will soon come around to our way of thinking if they wish to remain in office, for in reality the people are the power and if we stand as one, it would be very fool hardy for any government to continue ignoring our wishes. We all bear the responsibility for what is to transpire in the future and in truth our actions govern what will come to pass. If you want to see that your children and coming generations are given the opportunity to live in freedom and be afforded the right to heal themselves naturally, please join with me and together we can give our planet a new lease on life and not to mention save ourselves in the process.

By freeing the cannabis hemp plant, we will in turn free ourselves and when this occurs, it will be a new day for mankind. So let us act as one and soon we will find the better world, for which we have all been searching. The time to act is now and if most refuse to do so, then it can only be said that indeed we have become the authors of our own destruction.

Surely, one would expect that whoever or whatever created our species had something more sensible and meaningful planned for our future than just suffering and death. So I besiege all who hear my words today to help spread this message of hope so we can evolve more rapidly to a much higher level of consciousness. When this comes about, we should be able to live in freedom and plenty, while indeed remaining in good health during our journey through life, and this will finally allow us to fulfill the role, for which mankind was intended.

We were not put here to destroy this earth by being reckless and fighting over its resources. The true function, which we are supposed to be performing is to act as shepherds who will manage this planet properly and very soon now, for our own sake, I hope we will begin to do just that. Can we do better? You bet we can, and now all we have to do is find the resolve to bring it about.

Rick Simpson
Croatia, Europe 2012

CHAPTER 11

MAX IGAN: CANNABIS IN THE POLITICAL WORLD

A Speech Given by Max Igan to the Global Hemp Congress, Slovenia - August 27th, 2012

I have been asked to speak to you today on the subject of Cannabis in the Political World. This is a topic that is indeed close to my heart and it is one that never fails to raise my blood a little and so I make no apologies for any political feathers that may become ruffled by my words today.

I have heard a lot of good ideas presented today, and I truly commend the presenters. The information they have presented is very much needed and I respect the politically correct manner in which their presentations have been made, but please do not ask for, or expect any political correctness from me regarding the issue of the illegality of hemp in this very politically incorrect world. And as I said, I make no apologies for my words nor my stance on this issue today.

I would like to open this presentation with a quote:

"The real hopeless victims of mental illness are to be found among those who appear to be most normal. Many of them are normal because they are so well adjusted to our mode of existence, because their human voice has been silenced so early in their lives, that they do not even struggle or suffer or develop symptoms as the neurotic does. They are normal not in what may be called the absolute sense of the word; they are normal only in relation to a profoundly abnormal society. Their perfect adjustment to that abnormal society is a measure of their mental sickness for these millions of abnormally normal people are living, without fuss, in a society to which, if they were fully human beings, they ought not to be adjusted."

That was a quote made by Aldous Huxley, the author of *Brave New World*, just a few short years before his death in 1963.

And I would suggest to you now that the illegal status of the hemp plant, and the political, social, and environmental implications of that illegality is a true indication of the currently abnormal status of modern society to which Aldous Huxley was so eloquently referring.

When one looks at the myriad of uses of the hemp plant, and the benefit it has been to humankind throughout history - and this has been true for virtually all of recorded history, and I'd really like you to just breathe that in and let it sit with you for a while, ladies and gentlemen.

Just think about it... throughout ALL recorded history, this plant has been used and has been demonstrated to be a massive boon to not only humanity, but also to the environment.

When you really take in that one simple fact, and then you step back for a second to take in and to truly absorb the reality of its current illegal status, and the true implications of what that really means, well then that's when things begin to get a bit ugly, because that's when you begin getting into areas that people simply don't like to discuss. And I tend to do that on many occasions.

Because what is the illegality of hemp? Apart from ridiculous?

And it is ridiculous, as I'm sure most of you here in attendance already know - I mean just take in the big picture here, On one hand we have alcohol and tobacco, both of which kill tens of thousands of people each year, and these are both legal - along with some of the most pollutive industries on earth, I might add… all legal

And then on the other hand, we have hemp, a simple natural plant.

A plant from which, it just so happens, we can make the best quality paper and fiber products, particle board, building materials, hemp-crete, plastics and cellulose products, fabrics, essential oils, foods and medicines, and on and on.. You have seen some of the myriad of uses for this plant just in the short time you have spent here today.

It is a plant that will grow virtually anywhere with minimum attention. A plant that grows to full maturity in 3 months with no need for special fertilizers and that naturally improves the soil it grows in.

It is a plant that has quite literally served as mankind's companion plant throughout all recorded history… and in all that time, has not been responsible for the death of one single person ever, in its over 5000 years of recorded use.

And this plant is by law and decree… illegal, and we are told that this must be so….because of concerns for our safety no less…

When you truly step back and take that all into account, the illegal status of the hemp virtually *defines* the literal definition of the word ridiculous better than any dictionary ever could. Indeed when one truly looks at the issue from the correct perspective, ridiculous is simply the default conclusion regarding the matter.

And so the question must be asked… Why then is this plant really illegal?

And the reason is because were it legal, it would instantly free mankind from the financial shackles of some of the biggest, most pollutive, and most profitable corporations in the world today.

Mining companies, oil companies, timber, plastics, building, pharmaceuticals… all of these industries would suffer a dramatic reduction in profits were hemp to be made legal.

OK, so ultimately, its business, ah-ha, you say, we can protest, boycott their products, send complaints, and petition the governments for change… and these have traditionally been the steps we have taken.

But the truth is that no matter how much we do that, the position never seems to change… we just get reports back from the governments… "yes, we will be addressing that matter at the next meeting in June…." but no matter how much we attempt to bring about change by working within the parameters provided for us, it's always the same.

So why?

And the why, is the truly diabolical part of this issue, because the why, is that all of these companies came to power and gained the control they currently have precisely through legislation enacted by the governments we seek to petition.

And these are the same governments who enact the legislation that is used to prevent the people from having any real power and thus from ever having any real control over the matter.

And so, as a society, we flail endlessly against a wall of indifference hoping for common sense and freedom that never comes, because we are always working within the parameters of a corporate system that simply will not allow common sense and freedom to be part of this reality… due to concerns for our safety.

And if one really gets involved in this world, we find that it is not only this way for hemp, it's the same for every other serious issue that mankind is facing. It's the same if one attempts to do battle against environmental degradation, against pollution, homelessness, war, starvation, poverty, coal seam gas mining or corporate corruption.

And that's when it becomes clear that all of these so called problems are in fact actually symptoms of the one higher problem, and that problem lies within the foundation and structure of the system itself. A system that was apparently constructed by mankind, to service mankind's needs.

And no matter how we try to affect any real change within the system, we ultimately fail because we only ever address the symptoms rather than the actual problem and thus our response is compartmentalised, ultimately rendering it ineffective.

So, what do we do?

How do we inject common sense and freedom into a system that simply will not allow it?

What we do, is we shift our perspective to see the inter-relation between all these symptoms and we focus on the actual problem that is causing them.

That problem lies with the system itself and in the loss of the natural power than each human being on this earth actually holds within them should they choose to exercise that power.

Now, I could go into a myriad of ways to do this and to discover how powerful you all actually are, but that would require an entire presentation on its own and we would be here all day, so I won't go into that now.

But what I will say is that, personally, I believe the very first thing we need to do is to understand just what the system is and the first step we need to take is in coming to a clear understanding of what our actual relationship with government is. And this is a question that many people simply fail to ever ask.

In saying that, I'm reminded of a quote by Martin Heidegger in which he said:

"The most thought-provoking thing in our thought-provoking time is that we are still not thinking."

And that's what we need to do, my friends, we need to start thinking, we need to start realizing the truth. We need to remember who and what we are and the power that we the people hold as a community. If we choose to exercise that power.

Most people just take it for granted that government are our controllers and they don't ever question the fact, and they think this way because they have been trained to think this way via the thought processes instilled into them by a government-controlled education system. But the real truth is that we live in democratic nations, where we have government elected by the people, of the people and for the people and that what our relationship with those whom we elect actually is, is one of fiduciary trust.

It's that simple folks, we employ these people to act on our behalf and they are simply not doing so.

The truth is that those elected to govern are in fact public trustees whom we employ to manage what is essentially, the administrative arm of our society. They are nothing more. And I would suggest that all one needs to do is look at the current state of our world in order to realize that virtually every government in the world today is in breach of trust.

In fact I would even go so far as to say that the Illegality of Hemp is a clear indication of that Breach of Trust. Because the legalization of this plant would put a stop to many of the most pollutive industries on earth, be instrumental in helping steer the ship of state on a different course than the path of self-destruction it is currently on, and effectively set the world on a path towards freedom and abundance. And yet, at present this plant is still illegal... due to concerns for our safety.

My friends. This is breach of Trust.

And this is the pure and simple truth, regarding the illegality of hemp.

And so the real question becomes, how might this matter be dealt with.

Well the truth is the only way this matter may be effectively dealt with and in which remedy for this ridiculous situation may be found, is via action undertaken by the people themselves.

But again, How?

Sure we need to take action. But what is the action we need to take?

Overthrow the governments through revolution? No, not at all, because we need some sort of administrative arm due to the structure of our societies. Violent revolution has been tried in the past and in truth it has never effectively brought about and real change, and I am certainly not promoting revolution or the overthrow of any governments.

We need an administrative arm, but we need an administrative arm, (public trustees), that is both competent and reliable, but even more than that, we need public trustees who are both honest and accountable.

And I must say that it is a welcome relief to see that certain governments seem to be, at last, coming to their senses, such indeed seems to be the case with the government here in Slovenia and I commend them on the stance they are taking by allowing this congress to be held and in the support they are showing to this issue. I believe it is through the actions of small countries such as Slovenia and the examples they are setting that empowerment for other countries may be found, and in that empowerment, hopefully the encouragement, to then follow their lead.

And may I also say that the first world leader to act on this matter and commence an initiative to legalize hemp will go down in history as one of the true saviors of humankind.

And a responsible government should see the truth and reality of this. A responsible government should clearly recognize that as a species, we need public trustees who are both honest and accountable, but such accountability will only ever be achieved by a populace who is awake and informed enough to know what the true role of government actually is. And that role, is that of public trustee.

And the truth is that this is not unique to any one country but is a simply fact regarding the global community known as mankind and that effective change must therefore be brought about by action undertaken by the global community as a whole. Each group taking similar action in their own respective countries.

The truth, folks, is that hemp is and has always been illegal, not in order to ensure public safety but in order to serve a political agenda that is wholly subservient to corporate power.

The truth is that hemp is illegal because legalizing it would affect corporate profits and free mankind from the clutches of the system of contrived scarcity - because that is true the nature of the financial system that currently enslaves them…

The truth is that hemp is illegal because the system that we currently have in place is not designed to service the needs of the people but is designed to service an economic model that places the needs of the corporations, and the needs of the economic model above the needs of anything else, and that views mankind as the most expendable thing that exists within the parameters of the system.

Hemp is illegal because, under the dictates of the current political model, the entire human experience has been reduced to commerce and our mother earth has been reduced to a resource to be used for corporate profit in order to support an economic model that does not service the needs of either mankind or the earth we live upon, in any way, shape or form.

I believe an end to the prohibition of hemp can be achieved, but the truth is that it can and will only ever be achieved through action undertaken by the people themselves.

It can only be achieved through action by the people simply because most governments are simply scared to be the first to address the issue.

Therefore it must be done by the people, regardless of legislation enacted by public trustees because when such legislation does not serve the best interests of the people, then it must, as a matter of course, be contested by the people.

This is called democracy

Many governments may wish to change this state of affairs, such as the government here in Slovenia, but even these governments need the support of the people.

But what action can be taken against a government who fails to address this issue?

Perhaps the action that is needed may be as simple and direct as a peoples' mandate.

What would happen if the people of the world simply mandated that change is immediately implemented?

Remember, government is simply a collection of public servants whose job is to act as the administrative arm of the people. A democratically elected government is a group of public trustees. It is nothing more.

And a democratically elected government has no other choice other than to comply with a peoples mandate because were a government to do otherwise, then its action is nothing more than an open declaration of dictatorship.

Do we live in a dictatorship?

We the people hereby mandate that you, our public trustees, implement the following changes because to do so is in the best interests of mankind and the earth we live upon. You have 30 days to comply.

Should you fail to comply you have abdicated your right to govern and you will be required to step down, to then be replaced by a new group of elected trustees who will act upon the will of the people.

A peoples mandate circumvents government bullying. It circumvents legislation, which is simply the act of public trustees, seeking to replace natural law with their will. It does not leave the matter open for negotiation and it places the issue squarely on the table.

And we the people must do this because the need to do this has become just that, a matter of need. It is no longer a matter we can debate or leave to the whim of a what is essentially a corporate controlled system, because the world is in bad shape and if we fail to act on the matter we are, through our own negligence, risking life itself.

The action provided to us by simply viewing hemp for what it is, I believe, provides mankind with one of the greatest opportunities for effective change that we have ever been presented with, and the benefits this plant holds for mankind, are quite literally providing this opportunity to us, on a silver platter.

I sincerely believe it is high time for the conscientious people of this world to take the matter in hand, stand in the power of our community and peacefully, politely, and non-violently, simply do that which needs to be done.

As I have previously said, I do not desire to overthrow any governments, I do not even desire the arrest of the criminals within various governments who have ensured that hemp has remained an outlawed plant, all I desire is accountability and a return to some sanity regarding the issue of hemp and the political agenda served by its currently illegal status.

And I would like to leave you now with a quote by Howard Zinn:

"Civil disobedience is not our problem. Our problem is civil obedience. Our problem is that people all over the world have obeyed the dictates of leaders and millions have been killed because of this obedience. Our problem is that people are obedient all over the world in the face of poverty and starvation and stupidity, and war, and cruelty. Our problem is that people are obedient while the jails are full of petty thieves and the grand thieves are running the country. That is our problem."

Thank you for listening.

CHAPTER 12

A TIME TO REST AND REGROUP

After spending six weeks in Canada during the summer of 2012, I can only report that since I departed in 2009, very little has changed there. Everyone I talked with back home stated that they knew this medication worked; yet, they still seemed to lack the resolve to get together and bring its legal use about once more.

When it comes to the suffering of others, I may be a bit more sensitive than most about this subject, but I really cannot understand how anyone could allow what is currently taking place to continue. It is almost as if many appear to believe that this issue does not concern them, yet their friends and neighbors continue to increase the population of local graveyards at an alarming rate.

As long as we are content to reject what is obviously taking place, nothing will change. But what will happen when one of your own loved ones is diagnosed with cancer or some other serious condition and this natural medication is not available to heal them? Like it or not, this issue touches us all and no matter who you are, the day will come when you will be in desperate need of this medicine to save your own life.

I can only hope that in the near future humanity will begin to think a bit more clearly about this subject, for if this does not occur, we are lost. If we do not begin to behave more rationally towards this issue, indeed it can only be said that our days of dominion over this earth are numbered.

During the spring of 2012, I was contacted by a woman in Slovenia, who wished for me to speak at the upcoming World Hemp Congress, which was to take place in that country in August. They offered hotel accommodations and two thousand euro if I would attend; so to further spread the word, I decided to accept their offer. This was the only time that someone has offered me money to come and speak, but in the end I did not receive the payment.

After I returned to Canada at the end of June, I got in contact with Max Igan and since he was also interested in attending, I arranged for him to speak at the upcoming Congress. I had done two interviews with Max in the past and I was very impressed by the way this man handled himself while recording these broadcasts. I knew what Max had to say would have a very big impact at the Congress and I was really looking forward to meeting him in person.

I did not have the money to return to Europe, but our local credit union provided me with a demand loan, soon August 14th, I flew out of Toronto and returned to the Czech Republic. After a few days in Zehun, I traveled by car to Slovenia so I could attend the event, which was to take place. It certainly can be stated that Max lived up to my expatiations, but sadly the *World Hemp Congress* did not. When we arrived at the hall for the beginning ceremonies, it seemed that the only ones in attendance were those who had come to speak.

I was shocked that this event was getting so little attention, but I was soon to find out why. In the beginning, it appears that the Slovenian government were willing to fund the Congress, but then they suddenly changed their mind and backed out. After this had taken place, the woman who was organizing the event apparently panicked because she now lacked the required funding to make the Congress a success.

In reality, at this point, the Congress should have been cancelled but instead it seems the organizer thought the event itself, could generate the needed funding. If the Congress had been held in such a way that we could have appeared before large audiences who were not forced to pay over-priced admission fees, the outcome could have been much different.

Although the hall in which this event took place could only be considered well equipped, it did not have a large seating capacity. So the woman who had organized the event set the admission charge very high in the hope that she could cover expenses. Most individuals these days do not have hundreds of euros to spend on admission fees, so attendance proved to be extremely low. It's truly a great shame that this Congress was not held in a more rational way, for there were many important issues concerning this plant discussed at length.

To the best of my knowledge, everyone who took part in this event including myself received nothing for their efforts. Some of us had traveled thousands of miles from other nations and had spent a great deal of money and time to attend this Congress but in the end, it was all done at our own expense. Even though the *World Hemp Congress* proved to be little more than a fiasco, at least we were able to obtain some very good footage, which I am sure will prove to be quite popular on the internet.

It was in Slovenia that I first heard Max speak about a people's mandate concerning the medicinal use of this plant, which he said the citizens of all countries should sign and present to their governments. If our elected officials fail to react to this mandate and continue to refuse to respond to the needs of their citizens, they are then in breach of trust and no longer have the right to even claim that they represent their nations.

What Max is proposing sounds like a very eloquent way of encouraging governments to finally begin working on our behalf. I think everyone should take what he is saying very seriously, for playing by governments' rules in the past has achieved nothing in my opinion other than trying to stage a worldwide revolution, which would cause a great deal of needless bloodshed.

Bypassing their rules and regulations with a people's mandate is the only conceivable way, in which I feel this can be accomplished in a peaceful manner. We need this medication and we need it now, so please support Max and I in our efforts to get governments going in the right direction.

The time I was allowed to spend in the European Union was about to expire again, so since Croatia was nearby and I had many friends there, I decided to return to this beautiful country to do more lectures on this subject. In the spring of 2011, I had traveled to Croatia and during my stay there, I had put on a seminar in Opatija. In addition, I had also appeared on a very popular Croatian television show called the *Edge of Science*. This show is viewed, by a large segment of the population here and during the coming months, this same interview was aired several times, so I felt that this year we could very well attract even more attention.

With the assistance of Max Igan, Ben Stewart and local supporters, we staged another seminar in Opatija at the Grand Adriatic Hotel on October 13th, 2012. This event was well-attended and there was a never ending stream of questions from the audience regarding the use of this medicine, so I knew that our statements had made a very positive impact.

A few days later, we traveled to Zagreb and staged another seminar on October 21st, at the Faculty of Philosophy, which is part of the University of Zagreb. This event was also well attended and I was very pleased with the audience's response. The next day, on October 22nd, both Max and I appeared on the *Edge of Science* and I am sure that this show will have a very big impact once it is aired.

Kresimir Misak, the host of the *Edge of Science*, has proven to be a real pleasure to work with and I would like to commend him for having the strength of character to give this subject the attention it deserves on national television here in Croatia.

Before I left Zagreb, some concerned individuals arranged for me to have a meeting with an advisor to the Minister of Health. She was a very nice woman, but explained that under the current circumstances, she could do little as yet to back this cause. I must admit that all this came as no surprise to me, but at least it did prove that I had gained their attention. Perhaps once these TV interviews come out and the public begins to complain a bit more, the Croatian government may feel the need to react to their citizens' demands in the coming months.

For the time being, it seemed there was little more that I could do, so I decided to remain in Croatia for a short while to put the finishing touches on this book. On October 25th, Max returned to his home in Australia and I returned to the island of Krk to make this book ready for publication.

Since we put the first book out in the form of an e-book in July 2012, we have used what funding it is generating to help keep us alive and continue spreading the word. At present, my bank account is still suffering and my overdraft remains in place, but I did have enough credit left to get myself back home. I expect to have this book completed about the middle of November 2012 and then afterwards, I will return to Canada for a little badly needed rest and relaxation. After three years of traveling, I am now very tired and I have to take some time to gather my thoughts, which I hope will help me to determine what direction I should take in the future.

At present, I am rather bewildered as to why we are not making progress more quickly. "Cannabis cures cancer!" should be boldly stated on the cover of every hemp publication worldwide and they should keep putting it on their covers until this issue gets the recognition it deserves. In addition, those who are the real activists in our movement must begin to loudly state this fact to all who will listen, so we can raise public awareness more quickly.

I believe there will be a good number of those we would expect to speak out who will not, and that is when we will learn their true agendas. Not only do we have to contend with those who seem perfectly happy to stand by and watch others suffer and die because to do otherwise could affect their incomes. We also have to deal with another aspect of human nature, which vast numbers everywhere often tend to exhibit.

Many people seem to be more than content to sit back and wait for others to make the changes, which are necessary so they might reap the benefits, yet they seem to wish to play no active role in bringing about an end to their own suffering and enslavement. I cannot conceive of this actually taking place but if we should by chance fail in our quest to have the medicinal use of this plant once more made legal for the benefit of us all, it will be due to the behavior of these uncaring individuals who appear to think that everything should be done for them.

No matter what is to come in the future, we will all be responsible for what transpires. If the human race is to continue to exist, we now have the means at our disposal to do so. Should we choose to ignore the situation we are in and not begin to do things more sensibly, then wars, disease, pestilence, and starvation will be our constant companion, until the human race ceases to exist.

This would truly be a bitter and completely meaningless end for our species, since we have the potential in abundance to see that such a thing should never come about. At this point, it is still anybody's guess as to what will take place in days to come but surely we can come up with something better than what we have endured in the past.

Now the only question remaining for me is where do I go from here? I had the greatest respect and admiration for Jack Herer and I still intend to continue speaking out about cannabis hemp's complete legalization, until Jack's dream for us all to have free access to this plant becomes a reality. I have already been able to achieve much of what I set out to do on the medicinal front, for at present, due to the information we have provided, countless individuals worldwide have already experienced the wonders of this medication's healing powers.

All that is required for people to help themselves is for them to have the ability to follow a few basic steps, which will ensure that this amazing substance is produced properly. Since this natural medicine is now gaining so much notoriety everywhere in a short time, this medication will no doubt become readily available to those in need. The facts which we have brought forward concerning the healing aspects of extracts produced from the cannabis hemp plant are going to change the face of medicine and our way of life forever.

After spending Christmas at home, I have no idea where the mission I am on will carry me. But I do know of a couple of countries, which might be worth investigating due to the policies towards this plant that they already have in place and there may be other options, which could also arise as well. For the next while, my time will be spent trying to rejuvenate myself and while doing so, I hope to get my life back into some degree of order so I can continue the struggle.

There are around seven billion people on this planet and a large cross section of them now own computers, so this should enable you to easily understand why we are now being overwhelmed. We will leave our email address up on the website, but **please do not bother to contact us any longer looking for oil or other medical advice. We are simply not yet in the position to render any further assistance other than to provide the information and instructions, which we have already made available.**

To reach the greatest number of people possible, so that we might work together to quickly bring this medical madness to an end, I must now concentrate on doing interviews and shows that will attract the attention of the masses on a larger scale. In the interests of doing so, anyone wishing for me to do an interview can still e-mail us at our website or I can be contacted on Facebook and Twitter. I am very sorry, but in the future, interviews will be about all I will really have time to handle.

I have already accomplished much more than I ever would have thought was possible, so maybe at present it might be best to just relax for a while and wait for all the dust to settle. Many individuals are making all kinds of claims about the oils they are producing, using methods other than what I recommend. There always seems to be this ongoing controversy about whose method is best and which produces the most medicinal oils.

In the interest of saving lives and clearing up all of this misinformation in a short time from now I hope to present the public with proof concerning the potency and purity of oils I know how to manufacture. Of course, the potency really depends for the most part on the quality of the starting material you have at your disposal, but obviously, purity is also an important factor.

If all goes well in the coming months, I hope to set some standards, which all oils deemed fit for human consumption can be measured against. Then when someone produces oil, they can take it to a test facility to determine how close it comes to the standards, which have been set. In the near future, millions more will begin to use this medication. So we need quality control and standards put in place as quickly as possible to protect the public from those who would try to sell them an inferior product.

I am not saying that the standards I hope to put in place cannot be raised and I invite anyone who may think they can set the bar even higher to please show us all how to do so. Knowledge, which can help humanity, should not be held back; instead it must be recognized, embraced, and then acted upon. If we begin to do this, in no time at all, our overall health and well-being will improve dramatically.

As we progress into this new era of understanding, a great many things will change. Still there is little reason to panic, for this is the path we must follow if we are to evolve into something better than we have been in the past. Change can be upsetting for many but if we simply work together with a common goal, we should be able to make the transition into a better way of life quite easily.

I think by now many are finally coming to realize that if change is to take place, it will be we ourselves who must bring it about. History shows that we have never had much success in finding leaders that we can put our faith in and for the most part, we have simply replaced one tyrant with another. I think at present many would agree that if this is the best we can do, then perhaps it is just not good enough.

To rectify this situation, the majority of us must rediscover the same level of understanding, which individuals who wrote such things as the American Constitution had in abundance, for it is certainly obvious that they had a much better understanding of the rights and freedoms that people everywhere should have than those who control our existence do today. We need a new set of rules to live by, which do not infringe upon our rights and freedoms as humans. In addition, we require open and honest representation on the part of those we deem fit to put in positions of authority. This would ensure that our governments are never again given the opportunity to run amuck with our trust, as they have in the past.

If you want a real future for yourselves and your children, it is time to do a bit more than just complain about our situation. Get together with other like-minded individuals to form groups; then we may be able to organize them into a vocal force that governments will find impossible to ignore, should they wish to remain in power.

We are the human race and we can control our own destiny if indeed we choose to use the power we have at our disposal, so the choice is now ours to make. Do you want to be able to live in a decent environment and be afforded the right to protect the health of both you and your children? Or would you prefer to see us all trying to survive in this poison hell, which we ourselves have helped to create? The way we will exist in the months and years to come is now in our hands. I can only hope that we as a species will be able to overcome our self-destructive ways and in time we can all work together to build a better tomorrow.

Up until the present, no government has offered to allow me the opportunity to further my research, nor has anyone been willing to supply the funding, which would be required. For the most part, it was clearly the role that I and other concerned individuals played in making the public aware of what benefits medicines produced from cannabis hemp can really have, which has finally focused so much attention on this issue.

There appears to be no question that researchers, drug companies, and governments knew all about the hemp plant's healing abilities for a great many years. Yet, through their twisted sense of reasoning, which required that the public remained unaware of the truth, they decided to keep this information hidden from the general population.

If I and others had not exposed it all, I really doubt if anything would have happened in regards to this medication's use and the public would still be unaware of what was really being done to them. Now sadly it seems drug companies and many others are hoping to make huge profits from this natural oil's healing abilities regardless of the fact that I was the one who introduced its healing properties to the world and it was not my intent for any of them to profit from this knowledge.

It appears that no country is yet prepared to allow me the opportunity to manufacture these highly medicinal extracts, which I am well versed in producing. This may possibly have something to do with my lack of formal education and these governments might be seeing this as an excuse they can use to postpone the inevitable, while maintaining the status quo for their rich friends.

No matter what may be the case, I obviously do not possess the medical background that many of these highly educated medical professionals have acquired. But what good is such training, if all they know about medicine revolves around treating patients with chemicals and poisons?

Under these circumstances and after dealing with thousands of patients who have used these extracts to treat all kinds of different illnesses, I feel that when it comes to healing I am more than capable of holding my own against any doctor. For I already know I will achieve better results due to the fact that the medications I use work and I am aware of how to produce highly medicinal oils, which have amazing healing powers that most of these pill pushers can only dream about. In addition, once you realize how much damage these doctors have been doing to their patients, who in their right mind would then put any trust in what they are saying? These are the same individuals who should have brought this information out years ago, so how could we possibly expect them to do what is right now? Perhaps in the near future when I show the world the medicinal potency and purity of oils, which I know how to manufacture using a new method I am developing, things may change somewhat.

For the next few weeks, I intend to rest up while I am waiting to see what takes place in government circles around the globe. With any luck at all, the right door might just open and if it does, I will then be able to demonstrate my ability in regards to producing this substance properly. Until this actually happens, rest assured that I am still doing my best to see that patients have access to this wonderful healing substance as quickly as possible.

Our day of salvation will soon be at hand and in a short time most of our suffering should come to a halt. In the meantime, all we can do is continue on with our struggle in the hope that we can bring this all to an end quickly. Even though we have not yet achieved our goal, I want everyone to know that I still feel there are much better days ahead for the human race and I wish everyone all the best that life has to offer.

Rick Simpson
November 11th 2012

About the Author

Rick Simpson has for years now been a household name to anyone who has ever heard about the healing properties of cannabis oil or considered it as an alternative treatment where pharmaceuticals have failed.

A retired power engineer who worked for 25 years in Canada's medical system, Rick Simpson after suffering a severe head injury in 1997 took all the medications doctors prescribed, yet their side effects did nothing but harm. In desperation, he turned to the use of self-produced cannabis extracts and quickly found that he rediscovered one of the greatest natural medicines that can cure and control many different illnesses. Most notably, he is known for the testimonies of thousands of people who were cured or were able to put their illness in remission having used cannabis extracts produced based on his method. Today, these extracts are usually called RSO or Rick Simpson Oil while Rick, for his rediscovery, is often considered to be the grandfather of cannabis oil.

While still living in Canada, Rick was giving the oils he was producing for free having been growing cannabis plants in his own back yard. He never even tried to patent the method he used to produce the oil as he felt this was information which needed to be shared with everyone and not kept for oneself or used for profit.

Rick Simpson put up the phoenixtears.ca website in 2004 to spread the knowledge about the healing abilities of cannabis extracts. He has also written two books on that subject 'The Rick Simpson Story', his autobiography which relates the story of his rediscovery and 'Rick Simpson Oil - Nature's Answer for Cancer', which focuses more on patient experiences with different serious conditions.

For more than a decade he has been fighting for the repeal of all laws concerning the regulation of cannabis use with the aim of making it once again freely accessible to all. He has held many lectures on the subject worldwide and received numerous awards in recognition of his efforts and struggles, as well as for the impact his work has had on the changing legislation concerning cannabis in many countries around the world.

More information about Rick Simpson and his work can be found in the other book that Rick has put out: "**Phoenix Tears – The Rick Simpson Story**" and it is available at **www.simpsonramadur.com.**

The only two websites Rick Simpson is affiliated with are:

www.phoenixtears.ca
&
www.simpsonramadur.com

Made in the USA
Columbia, SC
07 June 2023